Being

A MANUAL FOR LIFE

Being

A MANUAL FOR LIFE

Bennet Wong and Jock McKeen

THE HAVEN INSTITUTE PRESS 2013

THE HAVEN INSTITUTE PRESS

240 Davis Rd
Gabriola Island, BC
VOR 1X1 Canada

www.haven.ca

Being: A Manual for Life

First edition (*A Manual for Life*) 1992.
Second edition (*The New Manual for Life*) 1998.

ISBN 978-0-9784618-3-6

Designed and typeset by Toby Macklin
www.tobymacklin.com

Original cover artwork by Mary Sullivan Holdgrafer,
photographed by Seann Childs of LightArt Photography.

In memory of Ian McWhinney

Scholar, teacher, friend

Contents

Preface to the 2013 Edition

Foreword to the 1992/98 Editions by Gerry Fewster

Prologue: Waiting at the Station 17

PART I: DISCOVERING STRENGTH

1 The Failure of Success: Self-Hate and Self-Compassion 21

2 The Power-Strength Continuum 32

3 More Distinctions on the Power-Strength Continuum 44

4 Self-Esteem, Mirroring and Self-Compassion 57

5 Entitlement 61

PART II: IN THE FACE OF ANXIETY

6 Existential Anxiety: The Challenge of Being Alive 69

7 Location: Finding Freedom in Time and Space 75

8 From Objectification to Inclusion: Bridging the Gap 85

PART III: RELATIONSHIPS

9 Intimacy 95

10 A Model for Communication 104

11 Anger: An Example of Sharing Feelings Responsibly 112

PART IV: HEALTH AND HEALING

12 Learning in Illness and Health 119

13 Allergies and Phobias: A Matter of Self-Definition 127

14 Multiple Sclerosis: An Example of our Approach 134

15 Disengaging Depression 149

16 Energy Concepts and Health 159

PART V: ISSUES AND OPPORTUNITIES

17 Change and Transformation: The Risk of Becoming Yourself 169

18 Beyond Therapy: Discovery and Growth in Helping Relationships 175

19 From Survival to Discovery: Options in the Wake of Abuse 183

20 Memories of Abuse: A Call for a Balanced Perspective 195

21 "Truths" (Not) To Live By 203

22 Spirituality, Religion and Meaning 213

Epilogue 220   Notes 223   Index 231

Preface to the 2013 Edition

Being: A Manual for Life is an extensively revised edition of a book we first published more than 20 years ago. The original, *A Manual for Life* (1992), and a further iteration, *The New Manual for Life* (1998), were written to accompany programs we created at The Haven, namely Come Alive and Living Alive Phase I. Another book, *The Relationship Garden*, was intended to complement Living Alive Phase II and Relationships (and later informed the creation by Haven faculty of the Couples Alive series). In these books, we tried to blend theory and practical ideas, and ended up with two books with considerable overlap, assembled over time. We have been gratified with the response people have had to these books, both in their English language versions and in their Chinese translations. They contain the central ideas of our work over more than four decades. We edited the original works ourselves, with some constructive criticism from friends and associates. We have always wanted to return to these, to bring more integration to them. Until now, we have not managed to do so.

When we finished *The Illuminated Heart: Perspectives on East-West Psychology and Thought*, we found ourselves much more satisfied with the degree of integration of this book. Having a sage and provocative editor in Toby Macklin simply brought us a finer product. With all our editing dialogue, we managed to display much more clearly many of the theoretical considerations which had been buried in the former books.

Returning to *The New Manual for Life* and *The Relationship Garden* has been somewhat like a major housecleaning, where you throw everything out onto the front lawn of your home, and decide what you want to bring back in, and where the saved items should go. Remarkably, as we have worked with Toby in this process, we have come to see that these two books are better companions to each other than we had previously realized. So, we have removed most of the duplication, and instead asked the books to get married to each other. Thus, now they stand as a unified pairing.

For continuity and clarity, we wanted to keep the original titles. And yet, we also wished to reflect the considerable changes that have occurred in this intensive re-working. These are indeed two new books, rather than retrofitted versions of the old ones; yet the ideas and models we address are largely the same as the ones in the original volumes. Our solution has been to give each book a one-word title, and retain the original title as a subtitle. Thus, we now have *Being: A Manual for Life*, and *Joining: The Relationship*

Garden. We have studiously kept the parts of the original books that people have found useful, and tried to show the associations between them more clearly.

The editing and publication of these books have been made possible by The Haven's Education Development Fund; Andrew Bing was the major contributor to that fund. Our special thanks to Andrew and The Haven for supporting this project. We are grateful to Wayne Dodge for his precise and careful proofreading, and to Mary Sullivan Holdgrafer for the beautiful artwork on the covers of both *Being* and *Joining*. And especially, our appreciation goes to Toby Macklin for his deft editing, honouring the spirit of the original texts while consistently urging for clarity.

We are very happy with the result of this process, to render two companion volumes with a consistent voice, and with a flow of ideas between them. We hope you find them useful and enjoyable.

Bennet Wong and Jock McKeen
Nanaimo, BC, February 2013

Foreword to the 1992/98 Editions

By Gerry Fewster

Teacher, writer and therapist, Gerry Fewster is the author of Ben and Jock
(Oolichan Books, 2001).

When I first became convinced that my survival depended upon my willingness and ability to make things right for others, I had no words or concepts that might account for this experience of infancy. Even now, I have
only the faintest understanding of how these pre-verbal images were transformed into personal choices that drew me away from my thespian fantasies and carved out an uneasy career as a professional helper.

As a young student of psychology I was rebuked by my teachers for
polluting their pristine rivers of knowledge with reflections of the "irrelevant" and seemingly chaotic experience of my own life. By the time I
entered the hallowed halls of Graduate School, however, I had learned to
rise above these undisciplined urges and join my fellow students in their
relentless search for the truth about the nature of the organism. I entered
practice wondering if these organisms would, in fact, conform to my newly
acquired body of knowledge, while fearing the possibility that they might
not respond to my carefully rehearsed interventions.

Fitting my clients with their "diagnostic" strait-jackets was relatively
easy although it was painfully obvious that, once contained, I had no key
with which to set them free. For the first year or so, I was quite prepared
to accept that their apparent resistance to change was something to do
with me and I applied myself diligently to mastering the tools of my trade.
In later years I urged myself to believe that it was their own pathological
obstinacy that thwarted my efforts, but the strain of trying to fix other
lives was becoming increasingly unbearable. By the time the humanistic
movement was in full swing in the late sixties, I was ready to look at some
alternative ways of meeting my needs and bolstering my struggling ego.
Here was a new orientation with some new techniques. Again, I prepared
myself to become the expert in my chosen field. I tried to fill my emptiness with more concepts and more words, and continued to maintain the
illusion.

By the time I met Bennet Wong and Jock McKeen in 1985, I was barely
hanging on. My role as a professional offered only the flimsiest veil of

assurance and the "irrelevant and seemingly chaotic experience of my own life" was speaking back to me in a foreign tongue. Encouraged by my partner Judith, I participated in one of the programs offered by The Haven and, fighting my own resistant pathology, I slowly – very slowly – began the painful task of unravelling the chronicles of an unreflected life by coaxing myself into the experience of the moment. In this strange, and sometimes empty, place, an emerging sense of Self began to challenge the textbook beliefs of my Psychology.

Somewhere along the way, I had failed to grasp the simple empirical principle that the nature of phenomena changes in accordance with the stance of the observer. Slowly it began to dawn on me that other lives could only be understood in relation to my own life and that I was using my quest for objectivity to obscure the totality of one side of the equation. It was obvious to me that Ben and Jock were not only exploring this other side but had thrown the doors of learning wide open by revealing one side to the other, first in their own relationship and then in their work with program participants. I had never witnessed or experienced anything like it before and my excitement, tempered by fears about what I might discover, challenged my courage to leap across the chasm. But Englishmen prefer to build bridges.

When Ben and Jock graciously agreed that I should write a book about them and their relationship, I had in mind that I could use their trestles to pick my way across and begin the search for my own wisdom. It was clear from the outset that this would be no true biographical or pure scientific enterprise and I marvelled at their willingness to have their lives projected through such a crude and contaminated filter. Despite their assurances that "truth" is an experiential reality, I harboured serious doubts about the integrity of my "investigation." Then it occurred to me that my fascination with the relationship of Bennet Wong and Jock McKeen could become a legitimate scientific enquiry, but only as long as I was prepared to examine my own experience in the process. Whatever the beliefs of my old academic mentors, I was obliged to explore the world of my own subjective experience.

I am now convinced that a true psychology must reach down into the core of the lived experience – from the unheralded moment of spiritual enlightenment to the habituated minutiae of daily life. From here, our most cherished and time-tested concepts must remain open and responsive to the raw experience of being. It is from this foundation that Wong and McKeen have carved out their own beliefs, using philosophy and theory only when these abstractions fit the data – "until further notice." It is for this reason that *A Manual for Life* represents a radical and unique contribution to the literature.

Philosophers of the phenomenological tradition certainly have stressed the primacy of subjective reality and many psychologists have attempted to speculate about the nature of the experiential world. But philosophy has generally remained cold and distant while humanistic psychology has failed to produce the necessary analytic methodologies. In both cases the issues have been reduced to untestable polemics designed to challenge the so-called "scientific tradition." Meanwhile, those who have constructed their "knowledge" from Newtonian physics and Cartesian dualism have continued to abstract the life from the very lives they purport to study. *A Manual for Life* neither negates nor embraces these positions.

In the work of their own lives, Wong and McKeen have simply moved beyond the tedious debates that have separated the various schools of thought. Through their courage to confront the "isness" of their own experience they have detached themselves from the closed world views of philosophical prescriptions and, in their commitment to the integrity of their own truth, they have avoided the "rightness" and "wrongness" of academic psychologizing. Above all, within their own relationship, they have created a living experimental laboratory with standards of discipline and rigour capable of intimidating even the most zealous scientist-practitioner.

For many years now, Bennet Wong and Jock McKeen have been sharing their work and their world with those who come to participate in their programs on Gabriola Island. Their respect for each individual experience, combined with the elegance of their methods, serves to create a place of learning in which the shared truth of individual lives generates a constant flow of living data. Over these years they have meticulously sifted through the grist of personal and collective experiences in the development of their own ideas about our place in the universal order. Up to this point, the intensity of their engagement in this process has left little time for writing but their decision to publish *A Manual for Life* represents an important step toward sharing some of these ideas with other students of life. Hopefully, it is only a beginning.

As editor of *The Journal of Child and Youth Care* I was delighted to have had the opportunity to participate in this project. Having published a number of fine articles contributed by these authors, I jumped at the prospect of assisting in the publication of this volume and, like many Wong and McKeen watchers around the world, I have no hesitation in asking for more.

Being

A MANUAL FOR LIFE

Prologue
Waiting at the Station

By Bennet Wong

Most people seem to believe that destiny has some particular goal for them, that they were meant to become something special. To such persons, the task in life is to discover exactly what that goal is, to figure out the destination before being prepared to commit time and effort to getting there. This is a common life-stance among adolescents, who believe that education is a waste of time until they decide on an occupational goal. Many people live much of their lives in this immature pattern, whiling their time away until they know their exact destination.

In effect, these people believe that there is a specific train that will carry them to a particular locus of success; so they wait in the train station watching all the trains (opportunities) go by, entertaining themselves at the computer games with all the other waiting people. They might closely examine each passing train to see if it is the right one; but, because the destinations are never clearly marked, each train passes without being boarded.

In the station, these waiting people become restless and discontent, wondering when they will be given specific instructions about which train to catch. Even when they are advised to board a specific train, they find fault and raise doubts rather than taking the risk of embarking. They are afraid of wasting time by getting on the wrong train – they fear that they might arrive at a wrong destination and then have to return to this station to catch the right train. So trains keep passing them by. Yet they do nothing but waste time in the train station.

What such people do not realize is that all of the trains have the same destination – death. They may have different itineraries, with different stop-offs en route (for example, a different career); but ultimately, the terminus is the same. That being the case, these people would do well to board the very next train, take the first opportunity to become involved with the activities on the train, and be present for the trip. If they were to do so, they would notice their fellow travelers, the ever-changing passing scenery, and the pleasure of the motion of the train. While on the train, their challenge would be to discover creative uses of time and talents, especially in relationship to the other passengers.

An important element in selecting a train to board would be the character of the passengers already on board. Are they serious minded or revellers, musicians or poets, relaxed or tense, morally righteous or libertarians? These qualities will give some clue to the atmosphere that might be expected on a prolonged journey.

Giving up the investment in a future goal allows a person to enjoy the journey in the present. At any of the stops, it is possible to get off a particular train and board another. The danger in disembarking is that one might once again get stuck in the waiting room of another train station — to become uninvolved — instead of throwing oneself onto another passing train, to have yet another new experience!

Part I

The Discovery of Strength

Yesterday I met a whole man. It is a rare experience but always an illuminating and ennobling one. It costs so much to be a full human being that there are very few who have the enlightenment, or the courage, to pay the price – one has to abandon altogether the search for security, and reach out to the risk of living with both arms. One has to embrace the world like a lover, and yet demand no easy return of love. One has to accept the pain as a condition of existence.

Morris West[1]

1 **The Failure of Success: Self-Hate and Self-Compassion**

In our years of working with people, we have become aware of a very common dilemma. Most people we have met have a vague sense of something being not quite right. And we ourselves have experienced this within ourselves. This experience is not always foreground; yet, whenever we look for it in ourselves, we find this sense of being somehow lost, or "not at home." Something is amiss. Many others have reported something similar to us, and we have been prompted to investigate how this comes to be. There is also the sense of having not accomplished what we should have, maybe of having done something wrong or just *being* wrong. We have come to see that this is related to being out of touch with our deeper nature, and an accompanying drive to do something to fix the problem.

The model presented in this chapter addresses this phenomenon and has been a cornerstone of our work with people over the last 40 years, as well as in our own lives. This model offers people a perspective on their situation and proposes an alternative to some of the paths they have been walking. In brief, we believe that in striving towards and failing to achieve an ideal image of themselves, people have lost touch with their own authentic natures and become trapped in a cycle of self-hate, the consequences of which are varied and often dire. The people who become most adept at this process of striving to achieve are often highly regarded; they are rewarded as ideal people. But inwardly, these successful people are often beset with loneliness, a longing for their inner nature, and pervasive self-hate.

We propose that people can choose to approach their lives differently by exercising their capacity for self-compassion. We developed these ideas over many years on the basis of work by Karen Horney, Theodore Rubin,[1] and others, and are gratified to know that many people have found new direction in their lives through the practical application of these concepts.

The Authentic Self, the Ideal Self and the Actual Self

We refer in this model to three "selves," the Authentic Self, the Ideal Self and the Actual Self. However, to be clear, these "selves" are not separate or distinct entities but constellations of a process. You might think of them as aspects of a person or elements of a process; they are not, however, static "things."

We assume that each individual is born as a distinct being, which we characterize in this model as an Authentic Self. As we've said, we use this reifying label as a convenience; however, it really isn't a thing, but rather a state of being. This being has a two-fold nature; on the one hand, each individual's "beingness" is distinct and unique, while on the other, it is an expression of the universal whole. In this way we are ultimately connected to one another, and to the cosmic process. So, each person's being is distinct, separate, apart, and at the same time joined or part of. Thus our basic nature provides for the experience of being both alone and joined. The individual aspect of the Authentic Self is apparent in the basic nature and characteristic personality of the infant. As many mothers will attest, even from the earliest days of life each child seems to express a unique and individual quality, a particular essence of the individual's being. Some might refer to this Authentic Self as the "soul." Whatever name we give it, it includes all the potential of that person's being that could come to fruition with time and future experience. Just as no two snowflakes are alike, each human being is unique from the beginning. And yet, though each individual is so particular, each Authentic Self emerges out of and remains connected to all other selves and to the entire universe. This is our spiritual nature.

From early days, most parents fantasize about what is possible for their growing children. In their earnestness to provide as fully as possible, they may dream of how their child can surpass what they themselves have achieved. They might think about how they can help the child grow and develop in order to be able to do this. This sets a process in motion that encourages success and achievement for both child and parent (the parent succeeds when the child gets it "right"). This is a necessary process, but with it there come deep problems. The parents' encouragement for their children to accomplish simple tasks and rewarding them for it with enthusiasm sets in motion an eerie dynamic. Faced with the parents' earnestness for them to achieve, often combined with an overt disapproval of their current behaviour, children get the message that they are not OK as they are, and that they have to do something to modify this. Even when the parental feedback is positive, youngsters get the message that the reward comes from achieving the Ideal Self, not in recognition of their native being. They see that the goal is to achieve, to become different than they are. The Authentic Self is apparently not enough. Thus, as children internalize the expectations of their parents and others, they begin to construct what we call an Ideal Self; this is an image of how they should be in order to please those upon whom they are, after all, dependent for survival.

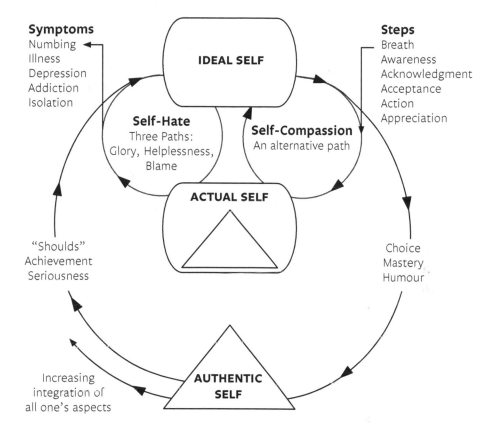

Symptoms
Numbing
Illness
Depression
Addiction
Isolation

Steps
Breath
Awareness
Acknowledgment
Acceptance
Action
Appreciation

Self-Hate
Three Paths:
Glory, Helplessness,
Blame

Self-Compassion
An alternative path

"Shoulds"
Achievement
Seriousness

Choice
Mastery
Humour

Increasing
integration of
all one's aspects

This is the normal course of events as a child matures. Expectations, demands, and injunctions that originate outside the child become codified, memorized, and incorporated into a self-regulating system of behaviour in the maturing person. What children want to do, to express the impulses of their Authentic Self, is often in opposition to what is expected by the parents. Those expectations become incorporated within the child's personality as a self-governing Ideal Self, and the struggle between Authentic and Ideal becomes an inner one. Once this process has been internalized, it occurs in the absence of the parents or any external authority. This self-controlling mechanism is well established in the first few years of life. In this way, children tie themselves into an early bind.

The expectations of the Ideal Self are often expressed as "shoulds"; to use Karen Horney's memorable phrase we subject ourselves to the "Tyranny of the Should."[2] This tyranny is absolute in nature: thus, "I should always be kind," "I should always be successful," "I should never be angry," and so on. As we internalize these absolute shoulds, we set ourselves up for failure, since it is simply not possible always to achieve such ideals.

The result is usually some form of compromise; this underlies the development of the Actual Self. The Actual Self neither achieves the standards of the Ideal Self nor expresses the full nature of the Authentic Self. Nevertheless, it is through such a process that the growing child becomes relatively well-behaved, disciplined, and civilized. The child is prepared to be educated for its responsibilities as a future adult.

From the outside, this process may appear relatively peaceful. The youngster is seen to be growing up and maturing into a "good" child, a cooperative student, and a responsible citizen. After all, the compromises being made are not unreasonable; they are for the child's good, fitting him or her for survival and progress in family and society. Internally, however, the growing child is struggling to live as these three selves – Authentic, Ideal, and Actual – trying to satisfy all of them in order to maintain some emotional balance or ease, some sanity. This attempt commonly leads to people becoming trapped in what we call a cycle of self-hate. There are two main aspects to this cycle.

In the first place, people compulsively strive for their ideal, fail to achieve it, hate themselves for their failure, and try again. If they do achieve a goal, they will tend then to raise the bar higher and thus perpetuate the cycle. Secondly, at the same time as this sense of failure increases, so too does a person's experience of having abandoned the Authentic Self. As people increasingly attempt to behave more in line with their Ideal Self, and lose connection with their Authentic Self, they react with a deep disappointment that compounds their ever mounting self-hate. Thus people hate themselves for trying to achieve the Ideal Self, and they hate themselves for not accomplishing it. This self-hate finds expression in many ways, which we will examine later in this chapter.

A sinister process is at work here. As children we learn to disregard the feelings emanating from our authentic being, and instead devote more and more attention to pleasing others, and accomplishing. Increasingly, children relate to externals, rather than listening to the messages from within; and so begins a life attitude of pleasing, placating and performing. We identify this as "field dependency," the field being what is "out there" rather than within ourselves. The situation becomes even more hazardous because of the tendency we have already noted for people to internalize the field. Thus, for example, we may carry our mother's voice around with us long after she has ceased to be directly involved in our lives. As a result, we find it increasingly hard to recognize voices that are more deeply our own. Each time the child follows the dictates of the field (whether it is clearly external or has been internalized) at the expense of their own authentic being, there is a sense of loss of contact with the self, and a feeling of betrayal, abandonment and loss. This sense of betrayal is a deep component of self-hate. This is the dilemma that is set up for everyone in any culture where achievement is valued. We recognize that it is important to learn to listen and respond to others; however, among the consequences of this there can be a loss of contact with oneself, so that a person gets out of balance, and a whole constellation of problems can follow.

It is important to realize that the Ideal Self is a person's own creation. It is not merely imposed upon us by parents and society. We are not simply victims of our upbringings. Rather, children (and the adults they become) are actively involved in choosing, sometimes consciously, sometimes less so, those ideals that they will incorporate into the image of their own Ideal Self. Some of these choices are clearly related to survival needs; as infants we all learn basic ways we need to be in order to ensure that our mothers feed us and keep us warm. Other choices are related to gaining the approval or love that we want, and amongst these we make choices about priorities, what we are willing to forego and what we wish to incorporate.

Our colleague Wayne Dodge illustrates this vividly with a story from his own childhood. His father, a keen baseball fan, wanted Wayne to play baseball too, and would spend hours with him in the yard, throwing him balls to catch. But, despite his father's best efforts and intentions, Wayne showed little aptitude for the game and little interest, and did not incorporate into his own Ideal Self his father's expectations for him around baseball. Another family ideal, however, was music and Wayne responded to this with enthusiasm, gradually building into his own ideal image of himself the expectation that he should be a fine musician. In this way, the Ideal Self is a (limited) expression of the potential in a person's Authentic Self, as indeed is the Actual Self. For Wayne, the image of himself as a talented musician is an expression of his Authentic Self, as are his actual musical performances. Problems arise when we react to the disparity between Ideal and Actual with self-hate, knowing all the time that neither the Ideal nor the Actual is a full expression of our authentic being. Both are limited expressions of that authentic being, and as we focus in ever more closely upon them, we progressively lose touch with the range of our own potential.

Three Paths, and the Symptoms of Self-Hate

In our society, it is often the most driven and achieving people who ultimately arrive at the "top" to become our political and economic leaders or our media stars. Many of them are filled with self-hate and anger. However, this process is not limited to a small number of people at the top; to one degree or another, everyone is faced with the dilemma of how to balance these inner forces and tensions. Nor is this only a Western phenomenon; we have witnessed the same process operating amongst the many Asian people with whom we have worked, and indeed in other cultures as well. To develop the Ideal Self, people learn to adopt and play socially acceptable roles; these roles may vary amongst cultures, but all function to maintain the image of the Ideal Self, at the expense of the Authentic Self.

Three broad paths are commonly taken when people are caught in this self-hating cycle:

- *The Path of Glory*. People can deny they are in the cycle, or attempt to ignore its effects. They can continue to strive for their goals, forever raising the bar. They may achieve a great deal, but it will never be enough. At the same time they will become more and more distant from their own authentic natures.

- *The Path of Helplessness*. People can fall into despair or self-pity for having to contend with the inevitability and hopelessness of the situation, developing feelings of depression and anxiety.

- *The Path of Blame*. People can focus on blaming other people or institutions (like parents and other authorities) for having contributed to the creation of this dilemma, or they may shift onto others the responsibility for their failure to achieve their Ideal Self. They may become obsessed with revenge and retribution. The accumulation of inner rage can have severe consequences for the body and mind.

Whichever of these paths a person takes – and we will likely take different paths at different times! – a wide range of symptoms can result, some more characteristic of one path than another. In order to carry on working against their deep nature, people become numb, rigid or frozen. Their breathing pattern and musculature are constrained, and they do not experience the fullness of being alive or the pleasure of contact with others. People lose touch with their feelings, and their bodies eventually manifest symptoms, which can occur physically, psychologically or spiritually.

Symptoms of self-hate can include stress, depression, obsessions, compulsions and various forms of self-destructive behaviour. In their desire to numb themselves to the process of self-hate, people will often become addicted to some substance or activity; hence, at the core of alcoholism and other addictions and dependencies there often lurks a profound process of self-hate. Physically, a wide variety of symptoms of illness can develop; such a process often underlies allergies and other so-called boundary illnesses (such as we discuss in Chapter 13), as well as a host of other psychophysiological ailments. Phobias, too, often have such a process at their root. Spiritually, an emptiness or anomie might be experienced, a lack of direction in life, or a deep sense of guilt, and possibly suicidal thoughts.

It is ironic that frequently the people who seem to be most successful conceal (often from themselves) high levels of self-hate. We ourselves saw this starkly during a brief period when we appeared on television talk shows, sharing the interview space with movie stars and other famous people. They were so charismatic, and so full of energy and brightness that we were intimidated to be in their presence. However, we were surprised and humbled when numerous times, these famous people would come quietly knocking on our dressing room door to talk to the "doctors who were the life style experts." To our surprise, we heard a common story: these people were famous and successful on the outside, and yet their relationships were in disarray, they were battling addictions and other self-defeating behaviours, and they were profoundly insecure. The disparity between the outside success and the inner uncertainty was stunning.

As we have seen, it is often the most driven, high-achieving people who occupy positions of power in society. How these people handle their self-hate has many larger social consequences – including family dysfunctions, antisocial behaviour, social unrest, and even wars. But the same process is common to us all.

Another Path: The Cycle of Self-Compassion

Fortunately, there is an alternative to these paths and the cycle of self-hate. At any moment, the Actual Self is capable of relating to a situation in two ways. As we have seen, people can react with ambitious striving, and intensify the self-hate cycle. Alternatively, they can choose to respond with self-awareness and self-acceptance, thus setting in motion what we refer to as the self-compassion cycle. There is at this juncture the existential phenomenon of choice: although we are not to blame for how we got into the fix we're in, we are free to choose how to relate to it, and what we do about it. The Actual Self has both a self-hating aspect, and a self-compassionate one. People are free to choose at any moment which process they will inhabit.

When people become aware of their predicament, they can learn to accept themselves for the persons they are and realize that they have a choice about when to act on the impulse toward perfection and when not to. They may choose to love themselves, to ease up for a change, and pay some attention to their needs for relaxation or pleasure. This is the Path of Self-Compassion. We describe this as a cycle, and suggest some steps along it. These are contained in the acronym BAAAAA: Breathing (B) mobilizes the Five A's: Awareness, Acknowledgment, Acceptance, Action and Appreciation.

We have already noted how in order to work against our deeper natures, we tend to constrain our breathing. Choosing to breathe more fully and deeply opens up new possibilities; it signals and facilitates a willingness to experience what is happening within ourselves in the moment. As we breathe, we can become more aware of our patterns of striving. The next step is to acknowledge the patterns, to others as well as to oneself; this acknowledgment overcomes the rigid pattern of denial, frees up the fixation, and reconnects us with others. In this revealing of the self, acceptance is demonstrated and furthered. This can be carried forward in action, made through more conscious choice, which further sustains the self-compassion process. Reflecting on the process as they proceed, people can appreciate themselves for their courage in facing the inner struggle.

By visualizing these steps as existing on a cycle of self-compassion, one can remind oneself that the path is an ongoing process in which one may visit and revisit aspects of oneself and experience deepening levels of self-compassion and acceptance. In the diagram on the facing page we place breathing in the centre of the diagram to emphasize its importance throughout the process.

At first, the process of becoming aware and acknowledging may not seem to have an immediate benefit. But quickly, the process takes hold, and self-acceptance, which is at first only slight, becomes more familiar, and more dependable. One is challenged to acknowledge one's imperfections, which include the desperate struggle to prove oneself through striving and power seeking. This is frequently uncomfortable, since with awareness comes increasing revelation of one's incompleteness and sometimes embarrassing motivations. On the other hand, as one accepts this challenge, the fixated Ideal Self image begins to slip, to fade, replaced by a felt assurance

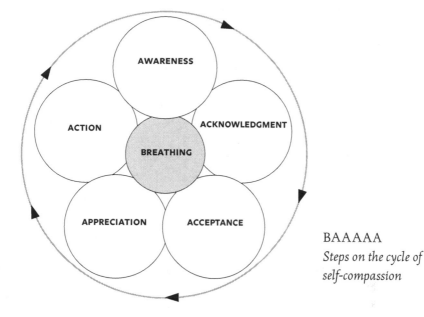

BAAAAA
*Steps on the cycle of
self-compassion*

of being more settled within oneself. The desperate isolation and loneliness of the achievement cycle becomes more background, and a sense of connection with oneself, with others, and with the entire life process become more and more rooted and substantial. And one day, the thought dawns, "I like myself for how I will open and reveal myself. I'm embarrassed about the shortcomings that I am revealing; but I like the kind of person I am that I am willing to do this." This is often accompanied by a warm feeling of settled satisfaction. What is fading is the loneliness, the sense of being numb or out of touch. I am in touch with me! I can accept myself for the Actual Self that I am expressing and revealing. And I can accept myself for trying so desperately to create and maintain this Ideal Self image. I have a warm feeling of compassion for myself for how desperately driven I have been to try to do this. I feel more at home in my own skin, and I feel quietly in touch with myself.

As I experience this, I catch a glimpse of something that I thought was long lost: I begin to see myself in depth. I get a glimpse of my genuine being! I am feeling myself, I am seeing myself, and I realize that the striving, the Ideal Self image, the Actual Self and its limitations, the courage to engage in this process, the feelings about myself ... all these are aspects of the one genuine beingness of me. I am all of this.

What began at first as a small (but courageous) sharing by acknowledging, followed by a slight acceptance of my striving and self-limitations, gradually grows in intensity and becomes a more pervasive aspect of every-day life. As this occurs, self-acceptance comes easier, the self-hate loses its intense sting, and my feeling of ease with myself grows steadily. The seriousness of striving and achievement is replaced with a warm sense of humour about myself and the circumstances of my life. At the same time, my view of myself expands and I experience and witness myself in all my facets: striving, Actual Self, Ideal Self, and lo! my deeper being or Authentic Self. The self-compassion cycle gets larger and stronger, and embraces the entirety of me in all my peculiarities and distinctiveness. Increasingly I become the master of my own life.

The image that comes to our mind is a waterwheel. As the wheel turns, the empty bucket dips down into the water of the deeper self and as the wheel of self-compassion continues to turn, more of the deeper self is carried up to the light of day, where the Actual Self and Ideal Self are. As the water from the deeper nature nourishes the Actual and Ideal Self, the whole process gains energy, and the wheel turns more strongly, plunging down into the depths for more. An integrative process indeed!

Some Dangers:
Abandoning the Ideal Self / Making the Authentic an Ideal

On this path of self-compassion, people have an opportunity to accept all aspects of themselves, including the struggle toward perfection itself. The Ideal Self has been constructed and groomed over many years; it serves a purpose and should be honoured. Trying to deny the Ideal Self is doomed to failure; furthermore, people who do so may end up striving instead to become more of the Authentic Self, which then becomes just another version of the Ideal Self! This creates new possibilities for generating self-hate. Even though the achievement ethic can become a compulsive trap, to abandon it also leads to fixation; instead we recommend learning to accept this aspect of our being and then make choices about how you wish to live.

The Power-Strength Continuum: A Teaser!

In the next two chapters we explore a number of ideas that are closely related to the model we have described here. You will see on the diagram on page 23 that we have included three pairs of words: "shoulds" and choice, achievement and mastery, and seriousness and humour. "Shoulds," achievement and seriousness are characteristic of what we describe in the next two chapters as a power-based approach to life, while choice, mastery and humour are more apparent when we approach life from a place of strength. The cycle of self-hate we have described is also related to the dynamics of power and control, while the cycle of self-compassion, and the revelation and self-awareness involved in it, are associated with strength. Both power and strength are important aspects of life; unfortunately, however, people often have considerably more experience of power than they do of strength. As we develop self-compassion through the processes we have described in this chapter, we have an opportunity to access much more of our strength and in this way experience a deeper sense of the fullness of ourselves and our connection with others.

2 **The Power-Strength Continuum**

Two Ways of Dealing With Root Anxiety

Newborns enter this world with the potential to become responsive, fully alive human beings, to flower into a full expression of themselves. The degree to which people achieve this in their lives depends on a great variety of factors (including family circumstances, the culture, and educational possibilities) that each person will experience, and the choices that each will make along the way.

Common to every one of us, however, is the experience as an infant of utter helplessness. Pervasive feelings of anxiety that accompany this helplessness persist throughout life, and seem to forever influence each person's future choices. No matter how well one does in life, this anxiety lurks beneath the surface patina of success. In response to the threat of existential or ontic anxiety (which we discuss in Chapter 6), people develop attitudes and qualities to prevent themselves from sinking into helplessness.

In this chapter and the next we look at some of these attitudes and qualities. We consider them as examples of either *power-based* solutions to the problems of life or a *strength-based* approach to its challenges. Power and strength, as we define them in this book, are ways of being and behaving in face of root anxiety.

The Power Solution

Western culture has offered people an education in acquiring power, which we define as "the state of having control over other people or things." Life is seen as a threat or a problem, to which power is the solution. Most people, often unconsciously, accept this as the most effective – and possibly the only – solution available, and their lives are thus involved in accumulating and maintaining power and control. Power exists in relationship to the external world, and to the objectified self. Power acquisition serves to cover over and compensate for the root anxiety; the more control that a person has, the more remote is the angst and the experience of helplessness. The anxiety and fear of helplessness are not abolished; they are only moved further away from conscious experience, buried deeper within the person. On the surface, people who have accumulated power seem self-assured and in charge; deeper within lurk the hidden anxieties that sometimes even they do not acknowledge. Since the power solution involves a defensive, controlling, objectifying posture, it operates – in terms used by Tillich and other existentialist writers[1] – against being, and towards non-being.

The Strength Approach

Another possible approach to helplessness, less well known and generally less valued, is for people to access and develop inner strength with which to respond to the challenges of life. Some refer to this as "personal power"; we prefer to use the term "strength" to minimize any association with ideas of control. Strength exists mainly in reference to oneself, not to the external world; it involves the capacity to accept oneself with all one's emerging qualities. Rather than developing methods of overcoming the opposition and threat of the outside world, people who manifest strength discover the qualities that they naturally have; they accept these qualities (sometimes resisting the expectations of others), and creatively design responses to life's challenges that fit their own situations. As people develop strength, they are able increasingly to experience intimacy with others. In contrast to power, which operates towards non-being, strength activity affirms being.

In this chapter we focus on some of the choices that are open to people in face of their root anxiety and the challenges of life. Although we discuss the qualities as pairs of opposites, the human experience is a mixture of both aspects; people can move on a continuum between the two. For most people, however, there is a tendency to choose one, and devalue the other. For example, people often choose power as a means of establishing security, thus devaluing the strength functions. In recent years, people involved in personal development have tried to emphasize the strength aspects, and devalue or deny the uses of power. We think that people can learn to recognize how much of each aspect is operative in any given situation, and move more consciously and freely between them in their own attitudes and actions. To learn about our nature, we need to become aware of both aspects, and acknowledge our relationship to them. In any circumstance, there will be varying measures of both aspects. Remember, this is not an either-or situation, but rather a continuum. Another way of saying this is that in different circumstances and experiences one aspect will be relatively more foreground while the other is more background.

We start by exploring the continuum between *standing out* and *standing forth*. This should give you a sense of how these distinctions work, which we hope will help you grasp the others we introduce later on. Indeed as we discuss standing out and standing forth we will touch on a number of other distinctions, which we explore further later in the chapter. In the following chapter we add still more distinctions to the mix!

We use this sign <--> to indicate that the terms should be thought of as existing on a continuum. Although most of us have more experience of the power end of the continuum, it is possible to move much more freely along it and increasingly to experience the value of strength in our lives.

Standing Out <--> Standing Forth

Throughout life, many people are obsessed with "making something" of themselves, "being important," accomplishing something that "matters," being "significant" or "counting." Frequently, family and society encourage a view of significance that centres on achievements in the workplace and success in the establishment of a stable and loving family; a respected and economically advantageous role in life is generally seen to afford the highest status. However, many people who achieve these goals still have feelings of emptiness or meaninglessness that they find hard to understand. It may be that they have confused the existential imperative to stand forth with a societal expectation to stand out.

Each of us is born with our own potentials; each of us is unique. Yet we are expected to develop and conform in the direction of the general mass of people, and at the same rate. When we fail, we are met with exhortations (sometimes subtle, sometimes severe) to conform. Always there seems to be an expectation that we "make something" of ourselves, that we become "successful," that we distinguish ourselves by "standing out" and being admired. It is as though we are expected to construct a life of significance, rather than to be significant. Toward this end, doing becomes more important than being. We may experience more security and a sense of control; in so doing, however, we severely limit our ability to face, and even embrace, insecurity and the vulnerability of being ourselves.

STANDING OUT

In our society, children are frequently taught to put others before themselves; such is the readily accepted ideal of "caring." At the same time, they are expected to stand out, to be distinctive, to be better than others. This is a contradiction, a typical "double-bind" situation, since one can only stand out at the expense of others.[2] For the sake of sanity, people must deny, repress, or rationalize this dilemma. Our culture encourages competition without acknowledging that those who succeed do so at the expense of those who lose. Winners are rewarded with authority, which gives them power over the lives of others. They earn a disproportionately greater share of material wealth and are afforded a higher public status than others.

Standing out provides the individual with praise and many other rewards, very possibly financial as well as psychological. What is little understood, however, is that such attention feeds the Ideal Self, belittles the Actual Self, and ignores the Authentic Self. People get attention for what they achieve or for the image of themselves that they present, but are not recognized for who they are. Though they may be given accolades, they are left with an inner emptiness, and a conviction of worthlessness. They are isolated from the others to whom they are compared. In reaction, other people often are jealous of those who are given so much attention.

People who stand out make objects of themselves and others. Although they may seem to be very energetic (sometimes hyperactive), they often lack a sense of genuine vitality and do not experience being fully alive. In their striving for success they frequently experience tension (which they may interpret as excitement) or a high-pressure charge (for example, as can occur with big business deals). They become obsessed with accomplishments, power, fame, and the notice of others; they objectify the people in their lives, who serve to fill their craving for attention and approval. By doing so, they become markedly field dependent, their self-worth tied to the amount of approval given to them by others. Because this emphasis on pleasing others is so common in child rearing, it is no wonder that people have a difficult time giving themselves approval and developing a healthy sense of self-esteem. Abandoning much of their Authentic Self, they concentrate on constructing an Ideal Self, and in the process generate self-hate. Their sense of pride is inflated, but their sense of self-esteem is low. They become driven to achieve more as they become trapped in a self-hating cycle. Unfortunately, they can only feel good about themselves when they are doing and achieving.

Because people who are devoted to achievement develop their sense of importance based on how other people (the field) view them, they tend to feel anxious that others may not be impressed or might even betray or abandon them. Hence, such people become obsessed with control. The more they can control the people and situations in their lives, the more secure they will feel and the better they will feel about themselves. This may become an issue for them at home; so long as their spouse and children are willing to be controlled by them, they feel OK. When other family members take steps toward independence or autonomy, they experience this loss of control as a great threat. In this way, power struggles are common within their families.

To stand out requires endurance, vigilance, control, effort, an obsession with external details, and constant monitoring of the expectations of others. People who stand out become independent (rather than autonomous), and individualized (rather than individuated); they remain greatly field dependent, continuing to rely on the attention of others for their self-esteem.

STANDING FORTH

When people stand forth they become autonomous and individuated. They derive their self-esteem from their own sense of jobs well done, from their own appreciation of their having given a task their best effort, of their being all they can be. To them, results are often not as important as the quality of the process of their activity. They are fully involved in whatever they undertake, and experience life as being full of interesting possibilities for exploration and growth., They are self-centred – that is, centred within themselves – but not at the expense of others. They remain connected, sensitive to the needs of others as well as to their own. They have a great capacity for empathy, while avoiding sympathy (which involves a condescension from an attitude of superiority). They recognize and respect the boundaries of others, and are interested in being vulnerable and intimate. They care about others without caretaking them, since they recognize everyone's potential for being responsible for themselves. Because they express themselves fully and responsibly, they manifest very little resentment or blame for others. It is only by standing forth in this way, accessing and developing strength, that people can experience true intimacy with others.

To stand forth requires the courage to be oneself. Standing forth involves creativity, awareness, presence, and focused attention, without sentimentalism (that is, overreaction or dramatization) or self-pity. People who have learned to stand forth keep in touch with themselves while entering the world with a fullness; they remain connected with the background from which they are standing forth. As they express themselves more fully, they are often inspiring to others. In their presence, people commonly desire to be connected with one another, being reminded of their own potential to be fuller and more of who they are.

To they extent that people stand forth, they demonstrate excellence in the world, in the manner in which they live and create; they appreciate the meaning of "coming into existence." They understand, accept, and appreciate the world of objects from which they have emerged, yet they are not controlled by it. Rather than becoming field dependent, they remain in touch with what they desire to do; they follow their hearts. Thus, they become more spontaneous, self-reliant, and self-motivated. They are more in tune with themselves and others, more fully human and fulfilled. Instead of achieving their tasks, they master them (that is, they fine-tune the skills that emerge from within, rather than imposing on themselves the artificial task of acquiring some skill for which they are not suited). They increasingly reveal themselves; so, they enjoy much recognition (as opposed to the attention given to achievers). They can experience a spiritual oneness without striving for it, or even naming it. As they stand forth, they recognize that they just "are," everything just "is," and this is enough. As Kierkegaard wrote: "To venture causes anxiety, but not to venture is to lose oneself."[3]

Exploring Further

We devote the rest of this chapter to investigating some of the distinctions we touched on in our discussion of standing out and standing forth. These distinctions all reflect the differences between power and strength approaches to life. Some of these we have already mentioned in our discussion of self-hate and self-compassion in Chapter 1.

Control <--> Vulnerability

Although the option exists to face all facets of experience, children are quickly taught to control themselves and the environment, minimizing vulnerability. To maximize pleasure and security, they learn to control their parent figures by adopting a pleasing attitude, and moulding their behaviour to assure parental protection. Of course, to control their parents, children must learn what the adults do and do not want, and then modify their behaviour accordingly. Children learn to control facial expressions, emotions, and actions, reading their parents for feedback of appropriateness. In short, they learn to control themselves in order to control others, setting a pattern for the rest of their lives. The prize is an increased sense of security and pleasure; the price is the loss of spontaneous expression, and the forfeiting of much authentic, innate experience. This becomes the prototype for subsequent relationships, and indeed for people's way of relating to all of life. Instead of accepting information from the external world and responding to it (that is, being vulnerable), people generally try to control themselves and their environment in order to gain more predictability. In contrast, if one is willing to be vulnerable, personal strength can be enhanced by one's willingness to respond to life instead of resisting it.

Control of both self and other involves power. Whenever people are prepared to experience all facets of life, strength develops. In the power attitude, life is an adversary. In the strength mode, a person is a willing participant in the life process; although there will be pain, uncertainty, and vulnerability, the individual grows ever stronger in the capacity to embrace these, along with joy and pleasure.

Non-being <--> Being

It is an existentialist position that the human condition involves a struggle to affirm one's being in face of the inevitability of non-being. As we note above, actions and attitudes that support power involve a high degree of control; they involve a defensive refusal to accept life as it is. In this sense they are deadening and anti-life. In existential terms, the individual is denying being, and striving towards a non-being state. Defensiveness, self-protection, deception, and other attempts to control the self and others are all movements towards non-being. Being open, vulnerable, acknowledging and accepting things as they are will move the person towards a state of being.

Isolation <--> Intimacy

Intimacy involves revelation, sharing and a willingness to be vulnerable. This makes closeness possible. If one attempts to control the other, and is unwilling to risk insecurity or pain, a depersonalizing distance and isolation result. If people wish to experience intimacy in their life, it is essential that they access their strength. We have much more to say about the development of intimacy in our book *Joining: The Relationship Garden*.

Objectification <--> Being Personal

When one is vulnerable, the individual person is revealed and personal. Whenever one operates at a distance in order to maintain power and control, both self and others are depersonalized and treated more as objects than as real people.

Power is always related either to an object or an objectified person, or, internally, to the "self as object." In either case this involves a process of depersonalization. Strength is personal, relating to the self and other in a human way. When people are willing to reveal themselves to others they can grow in strength through sharing feelings, revealing each person's viewpoint, and being vulnerable one to the other. By sharing their objectifications of each other, and of themselves, they can make the impersonal personal. This process is at the heart of intimacy. The communication model that we present in this book (Chapter 10) and elsewhere is a central tool in this process. We discuss the development of intimacy in depth in *Joining: The Relationship Garden*.

Achievement <--> Mastery

We described in Chapter 1 how people strive towards their Ideal Self image through achievement. Generally, their achievements are motivated by external referents, and often are not in harmony with their inner nature. These people often do not find fulfilment in what they are doing.

With strength, on the other hand, people develop a growing mastery and competence, which is not necessarily praised or even acknowledged by the external world. People in mastery are aware of themselves and the world around them, without investment in a particular effect; in contrast, people involved in achievement and control often are invested in a particular outcome, and show the insensitivity that accompanies power and dominance. Mastery results in genuine skill development (that is, development that is native to the individual's capabilities), whereas achievement accomplishes arbitrary skill performance (that is, performance unrelated to the individual's potentials).

Seriousness <--> Humour

The path of achievement and power is a serious business, demanding control of oneself and or events. In strength, by contrast, people can have a sense of humour about themselves, becoming more accepting and appreciative of their abilities and foibles, and of the circumstances of their lives.

Attention <--> Recognition

Recognition of another (Latin: *re + cognoscere* – "to know again") involves a personal closeness; giving attention objectifies both parties, and makes recognition difficult. In recognition we experience and acknowledge a person for who he or she is; in attention we focus more on what people do or on the ways in which they match what we want them to be. Thus recognition is associated with strength, being and fulfilment; attention is associated with power, control and achievement.

Security <--> Insecurity

People live amidst uncertainty. Each moment involves unpredictable change. To the infant, who is so dependent upon adult figures to provide care, this uncertainty is accompanied by strong feelings of anxiety, which evidence a basic concern for survival. This existential anxiety is a given for every human being. To alleviate the anxiety, children try to establish security in early relationships with adults; they learn to please their parents in order to gain attention and the assurance of continuing care. This is the beginning of the process we outlined in Chapter 1. To the child, the parent is a potent figure who can provide a buffer against the assaults of life. If the parent is pleased, the child will be safe and secure and will have minimal pain; if the parent were to abandon the child altogether, the child could perish. Thus, the cry of the infant expresses a recognition of the unpredictability of life and the dependence upon external parent agents for protection. This inner experience of insecurity continues into adult life, leading to dependent, power-based relationships. Although people could learn to accept the uncertainty of life, and develop strength in so doing, most usually try to control the external world to maintain a sense of security.

Field Dependency <--> Autonomy

When people try to feel secure by controlling themselves and others (often by pleasing them) they can be described as field dependent. They are reliant on outside sources (the "field") in order to feel OK. We learn this early on. Much of an infant's behaviour arises out of the fear of abandonment, which would threaten the child's very survival. To avoid this, infants learn to please and control. As infants, this was necessary; however, even when people grow up, they generally have not addressed this basic existential fear, and their field dependency (the necessity to please and control others) continues. Life therefore remains an adversary; they deny their fear in their urgent quest for control of themselves and others. In this mode, people are continually in a state of anxiety about the responses of others. Just as the infant fears the rejection of the parent, the field-dependent adult fears the loss of control of the other.

When people are willing to face and embrace fear, pain, and insecurity they experience less compulsion to react to the actions or opinions of the others in the field. Hence, instead of "playing to the audience," they can be aware of the field (see Field awareness <--> Field dependency below) taking others into account, but are able to make individual decisions and are in this way self-referential; this is autonomy. People in a position of autonomy are resilient, sensitive, and capable of compassion for themselves and others. Note that this is different from independence (see Independence <--> Autonomy below), in which a person ignores the field or reacts against it.

Independence <--> Autonomy

To be independent is still to be tied in reaction to whatever one is independent from. A person's actions are still based on their interpretation of the field, only this time in opposition to it. Hence, independence is not a true liberation. Many high achievers become independent, and may appear to be free and powerful; yet, in their attachment to the approval and attention of others, they remain tied and limited. They are independent, but not autonomous or free.

When people are autonomous, they have a centre within themselves. These people are free because, at the same time as being sensitive to the feelings and concerns of others, they do not base their own attitudes and behaviour on those of others.

Field Dependency <--> Field Awareness

In field dependency, one's actions are governed by the responses and reactions of the surrounding field; hence, one becomes shackled to externals and does not develop self-reference. When one is autonomous, one can remain aware of the field and take account of responses in it, without being dictated to by them; this position is one of strength.

Individualize <--> Individuate

To acknowledge and embrace one's insecurities means one can individuate. When people are power-based, they individualize; they may look free, and yet they remain tied to the external world both by their dependence on it and the requirement to stand out from it. In the process of individualizing (becoming an "individual"), one is not really growing in a free unfettered way. One becomes an individual in reaction to others; hence, the individual is tied to others. Thus individualizing is not an autonomous path of self-realization.

When one individuates, on the other hand, one is making free choices, and becomes oneself without reacting to others. The person who is individuating can move past the limitations of achievement into true mastery in life. This person grows into deepening awareness of self and others.

Individuating involves the actualizing of authentic potentials, and the referent is internal; individualizing has external referents and has little to do with authentic being. While individualizing people are either dependent (needing to lean) or independent (unable or unwilling to lean), individuating people are both autonomous and connected. They are free to be interdependent; they can freely choose to lean or not.

Taking Care of Others <--> Caring About Others

Taking care of others involves a role and a power orientation. To take care of others may be an attempt to control them, perhaps by having them feel grateful. It may weaken their initiative and maintain a tie to the caretaker ("You can't take care of yourself. You need me to take care of you"). A person may also take care of another in order to allay their own anxiety or control their own feelings. Caring about others, on the other hand, involves a consideration and concern that might not lead to any action; to care about another can involve feeling a great deal oneself and letting others make their own mistakes and find their own way. As with all these distinctions, neither one is good or bad. There are situations where caretaking is highly desirable – it is a paramedic's job, for example, to take care of a person who is having a heart attack.

Sympathy/Pity <--> Empathy

To feel pity or sympathy involves elevating oneself and diminishing the other; this is a power orientation. To empathize involves feeling close and identified with the other, often seeing oneself mirrored in the other; both persons are equal and are responsible for themselves.

Victimhood and Blame <--> Self-Responsibility

When people are responsible for themselves and their actions, they develop strength. They do this by accepting their own participation in events and acknowledging their own capacity to respond. More frequently however, people become involved in a dynamic of blame and victimhood, in which they attempt to place responsibility for circumstances outside of themselves. The blamer wants to make someone else responsible, and so too does the victim. In this way, guilt can be an objectifying and depersonalizing form of self-blame.

We say more about responsibility in the next chapter, where we are careful to distinguish it from being to blame or at fault (Being to Blame <--> Being Responsible, page 48).

Selfish <--> Self-Centred

Although the word self-centred is often used pejoratively, we ourselves point at its literal meaning to emphasize an important distinction. To be self-centred is to be aware of one's centre within oneself and to act from that centre while remaining aware of and responsive to others. It is thus an aspect of being autonomous (see Autonomy <--> Field dependency above).

Selfishness, by contrast, is more a power position, in which one puts one's own security and achievement first, at the expense of others or disregarding them completely.

Self-Hate <--> Self-Compassion

As we reach the end of this chapter, perhaps the relationship between the model we presented in Chapter 1 and the power-strength continuum is becoming clear to you. We think that self-hate involves power, while self-compassion encourages strength. In the power thrust to achievement, one abandons the Authentic Self, and self-hate accompanies the stress of trying to live up to the image of the Ideal Self through self-denial and self-control. In self-compassion, on the other hand, people grow stronger in their acceptance of all aspects of themselves, including their imperfections. We have more to say about this in Chapter 4 in our discussion of self-esteem.

In the next chapter we look at some more of these power-strength distinctions, which we find stimulating to both thought and action. In our own lives, we have examined these various phenomena and explored ways to choicefully shift different aspects of ourselves more foreground or background in different situations. Amongst the many rewards of accessing and developing our strength has been an ever increasing experience of intimacy, with each other and with other people.

3 **More Distinctions on the Power-Strength Continuum**

This chapter introduces some further examples of the power-strength continuum. As you read these, we hope you will consider how you locate yourself along this continuum in different situations and with different people. The programs that we developed at The Haven offer opportunities for people to become aware of themselves in relation to these distinctions. Frequently, people are well acquainted with the power end of the continuum. They are often dissatisfied with the consequences of this approach and come to programs looking for alternatives. We encourage them, therefore, to experiment and practice to develop their own strength. Though there is a time and a place for both power and strength, we believe that many people have severely limited the range of possibilities in their lives by thinking and acting predominantly from a framework of power. You can expand your view of the world and enhance your participation in it by developing your capacity for strength.

Minimize Pain, Maximize Pleasure <--> Accept Pleasure and Pain

From early on, people's experience includes both pain and pleasure. This duality is basic during each person's entire life. From the earliest days, however, people are encouraged to adopt a power orientation, to attempt to maximize pleasure and reduce pain: the world is a place to be controlled. When people are willing to accept both pain and pleasure, they can develop strength within themselves and experience the depth of loving. As Rollo May wrote:

> To love means to open ourselves to the negative as well as the positive — to grief, sorrow, and disappointment as well as to joy, fulfillment, and an intensity of consciousness we did not know was possible before.[1]

Political <--> Personal

To be political means to be involved in the use of power and control; generally, there is an investment in a particular outcome or effect. Note that this is a psychological definition of "political" and does not refer at all to governments and relationships between groups and countries. To be personal means to be revealed and vulnerable, willing to share one's own viewpoints and feelings without a particular investment in controlling a situation. Thus, in any given circumstance, people always have the option to be political or personal; sometimes they will bring measures of both to a situation.

Morality <--> Personal or Situation Ethics

In power orientations, there is often a morality that involves adherence to rigid definitions of right and wrong. When people follow a grid of rules and do not question themselves, they can be quite definite and decisive, but they act from a power-based, inhuman position. When people adopt a strength orientation, they remain more in touch with themselves and their values, at the same time as being sensitive to the concerns and values of others. Hence, each situation is open to personal appraisal, in reference to one's own ethical standards. In situation ethics, there are no fixed external rules; instead, individuals are challenged to continually reassess their own values in the context of each new situation, and to apply their values in a way that respects both themselves and others.[2]

Morality involves the duality of right and wrong. In a moral position, certain values and actions are judged "correct," "true," or "right"; others are judged to be "incorrect," "false," or "wrong." This can be very useful as an organizing principle in maintaining a social order. However, through attachment to this code society often fails to consider the needs and concerns of the individual. When people adopt their culture's morality without pondering the issues, they often lose the ability to think for themselves. Doing so may serve to reduce existential anxiety and provide a sense of belonging. But reducing anxiety also reduces life, and the spontaneous creativity and autonomy of the individual is gradually stifled. In this exchange, individuals gain a sense of security, while losing their individual freedom of thought.

When people adopt a non-moral stance, on the other hand, nothing is ever right or wrong; rather, people examine different situations carefully to determine their own personal positions, guided by their own value systems. To discover one's personal perspective on key issues, it is necessary to relinquish the security of conventional moral thinking and decide for oneself. Discernment of this sort does not necessarily mean abandoning society's moral guidelines; but it does mean thinking for oneself, rather than swallowing, without consideration, the predigested perspectives of the culture at large. To unthinkingly adopt the attitudes dictated by society is to accept a conventional morality; when one applies discernment to make distinctions and arrive at one's personal standpoint, this is the action of personal ethics.

Black/White Thinking <--> Shades of Grey

When people are in strength, they see the world in personal terms of self and other, rather than in the depersonalizing moral terms of good and bad. Consequently, individuals in strength recognize that there are subtle shadings in any situation, with much to consider; by contrast, when people are operating in the power orientation, things are clearly demarcated into the black and white binary motifs of good and bad.[3]

Guilt <--> Shame

Guilt is the feeling of discomfort and tension that is experienced by a person who has broken some imposed rule or law for which that individual has some respect. Guilt is always related to some external judgment, or some morality that has been internalized so that the external source need not even be present at the time of the infraction. The bodily reaction in guilt is to tighten, close, feel cold, and develop a state of tension. The person has a sense or fear of being caught, trapped, or punished. Guilt involves punishment for not living up to the expectations of others (or of an internalized judge). Guilt in this sense is a social convenience and may be used as a kind of social currency; by saying "I'm sorry," individuals can pay for their transgression, and avoid any further insight into the situation. Existentially, guilt is a state of non-being. It involves objectification of oneself as bad or wrong; hence, people are not present in guilt. By our definition, then, the commonly used phrase "Shame on you" is actually a way of telling a person you think they should feel guilty about what they have done; "Guilt on you" would be more accurate! Shame, as we use the word, is a different phenomenon.

Shame arises as a feeling only in reference to oneself, not to external sources. In shame, people recognize themselves exposed as they actually are; in this recognition, they often see that they are not all they could be. Thus, shame is always related to self-recognition, awareness of one's own expectations and the image of oneself. The bodily experience is one of flushing, of filling up with warmth, of being exposed, and of being without defence. Existentially, it is a being state. Shame involves revelation of oneself; hence, people are vulnerable and present in shame. While guilt works against intimacy, shame invites it.

Thus, we use the term shame in a very particular way. Our definition is different from that of John Bradshaw, for example, who wrote about the "toxic shame" experienced by abused children.[4] It also differs from that of Brené Brown, who speaks compellingly about the value of vulnerability but sees shame as an obstacle to it.[5] Although we, Bradshaw and Brown are all using the same word, we are clearly using it to describe different phenomena.

Our own use of the word is in line with ancient Asian perspectives. Confucian philosophy places a high value on the depth of life; Confucius said, "To possess the feeling of shame is to be near life energy." Some Buddhist traditions think of shame on the same level as love and compassion. This is the idea of shame we focus on.[6]

We have found, over and over, that people have meaningful and deepening contact when they are revealed. When people blush, we note that we frequently feel close with them. They are embarrassed; yet, in their vulnerability, we experience an invitation to draw closer. There is vitality and depth and energy in the exposure. This blush accompanies self-recognition; we recognize ourselves for what we are (and what we are not). This is the phenomenon we have labeled "shame." In this context, we agree with Christopher Ricks that "a blush is a very important spiritual experience."[7]

When couples have approached us over the years with the wish to go deeper, our recommendation has been for them to share experiences in their lives where they have felt the hot flush of embarrassment (which we call shame). Since people so rarely share the details of these experiences, the opportunity for newness and revelation is great. To us, shame is an experience of strength and an invitation to deepening intimacy and connection.

Sensitivity to Being Hurt <--> Sensitivity to Others

Sensitivity to being hurt by the actions or comments of others is a very powerful position; people who accept this can be controlled by the so-called "sensitive" person. We think this is actually insensitivity, not genuine sensitivity. True sensitivity to others involves being responsible for one's own feelings (especially one's hurt) without blame, and without attempting to control the other. One can be very aware and sensitive to others and still maintain one's own autonomy.

Shoulds/Injunctions <--> Desires/Choice

To listen to one's own desires and to operate from personal choice develops strength and autonomy; to obey injunctions ("shoulds") maintains power through field-dependent self control. Note, however, that to reject shoulds simply because they are shoulds may be an expression of power rather than strength, since the person is reacting in opposition to the dictates of the field.

Obligations <--> Responsibility

In strength, people act in a responsive manner, sensitive to the require-
ments of themselves and their surroundings. In power, people function on
the basis of obligations, which are predetermined rules of conduct that do
not consider the individual or the current situation.

Blame <--> Acceptance

To blame keeps one in the power role of a victim, where one is impotent
and oppressed by life. To accept oneself and one's situation permits a growing strength and a felt assurance in life.

Being to Blame <--> Being Responsible

It is a common misconception that responsibility and blame are the same.
When people are responsible, they acknowledge their part in any action,
either voluntary or involuntary, conscious or unconscious. If a pedestrian
is accidentally struck by a car while crossing a street, that person is responsible for being the one crossing the street, perhaps not being fully mindful
of the circumstances, perhaps even being in a self-destructive state. From
the framework of responsibility, both the driver and the pedestrian have a
story to tell that reveals each person's participation in the accident. But in
the terms we are discussing here, neither is to blame.

The framework of blame presupposes a morality of right and wrong;
some person must be at fault. The evidence is weighed to discover which of
the parties is at fault and which one is the victim, who is guilty and who is
innocent. From childhood onward, most people's experiences are framed
in these terms; so it is difficult to step outside this grid and view experience
from a morality-free position.

To take the example of infectious diseases, people are usually seen to
be the victims of germs, which are considered to be the perpetrators of
the illness. In the framework of responsibility, people are considered to be
responsible for creating the circumstances in which the germs grew, and
for the state of the body's vulnerability to that particular organism. The
illness process need not be seen in light of good or bad; it can be viewed as
a manifestation of a great number of processes in which the ill person has
participated, consciously or unconsciously, at some level of being. Nothing
and nobody is at fault; each person has a responsibility for participation in
an event, each with a story to tell, with individual purposes to be served.

The concept of individual responsibility for states of health and illness
is a central tenet of many holistic medical approaches. There are no victims; at the same time, nobody or nothing is seen as at fault. The focus is

on the individual's participation in the illness process from beginning to end, on the purposes that are served by such participation, on the story that is being told, and on the metaphor that is unfolding. In the concepts of complementary medicine, while traditional methods of treatment are being applied, attention is given to helping the person discover the reasons for creating, participating in, or supporting the illness. Unfortunately, many subscribers to holistic health become hostile to what help traditional medicine can offer; they sometimes even blame the person (sometimes themselves!) suffering from the illness. This guilt-producing attitude contributes to the perpetuation of the illness rather than furthering the healing process.

Walls <--> Boundaries

When people are operating from a basis of power, they are commonly willing to barter with life, using themselves as currency. They may appear to be well defined and clearly demarcated from others; however, they are generally hiding behind walls rather than living at their boundaries. Walls are brittle barriers, defences that keep the outside away; they are based on fear of the other and insecurity about the self. Unfortunately, walls not only defend; they also diminish a person's ability to make sensitive contact with the environment and with others. Boundaries, on the other hand, accompany the sense of self that comes with a strength orientation. Boundaries are resilient, flexible, and involve a sensitive relationship with self and other. People become increasingly defined through active choices that contribute to making boundaries. The Haven offers programs devoted specifically to this topic; and we look forward to the forthcoming publication by the Haven Institute Press of Linda Nicholls' book on boundaries.

Absence <--> Presence

Presence occurs with the vulnerability of strength; when one is involved in the invulnerability of power, the authentic person is not present. With presence, people locate themselves at their contact boundaries, willing to respond. Presence is accompanied by alertness, awareness, and fullness.

Roles <--> Authenticity

In developing the power of the Ideal Self, people learn to play roles, presenting a socially acceptable image to control their surroundings; because they are tied to others, role-players have a weakened sense of themselves. In strength, people are more willing to express themselves in a genuine fashion; hence, they reveal more of their Actual and Authentic being, and are more free of the external.

Reaction <--> Response

In power, people react to situations in impulsive, non-specific, programmed ways. In strength, people respond in particular situations, to specific people, with the fullness of themselves in a genuine, spontaneous way.

In the power orientation, others are objects to be controlled; in the strength orientation, others are recognized as living beings with whom one might engage. When people operate from the basis of power, they do not appreciate the world of others, who are objectified as roles (for example, as "my boyfriend," "my wife," "my son," and so on); in power, therefore, reactions to others are automatic, dogmatic, and rigid. In strength, there is a subjective, humanizing responsiveness that involves a discernment of particulars; thus it is possible to relate specifically and flexibly to the individual concerns, thoughts and feelings of others. In power, there is a dehumanizing, objectifying reaction, that obscures specifics, making discernment and flexibility difficult.

Hope <--> Faith

Hope involves a dissatisfaction with the present and a wish for or anticipation of future change. In hope, people are concerned with controlling events; however, by pitting themselves against external forces that might move a situation towards an outcome other than the one they hope for, they make themselves victim to those very forces. Thus, hope is related to power and control and is non-responsible. In hope, people are less present to what is happening now, and their personal growth and freedom are limited. Hope involves a denial of the present, and a moving away from life; existentially, hope is a non-being state.

We define faith, on the other hand, as "the felt assurance of the continuity of life." Faith emanates from within the individual and involves an acceptance of past, present, and future. Existentially, it is a being state that embraces both being and non-being. Fears of both death and life are diminished, as the person grows in strength, presence and responsive engagement with other people and external events.

Loneliness/Isolation <--> Aloneness

Aloneness is a condition of human existence that involves separateness and uniqueness. It is neither positive nor negative; it is just a given. Acceptance of aloneness permits people to feel their deepest nature and to develop strength. Loneliness is experienced when a person does not accept aloneness, and believes that existence can be different. Such a person walls off from the world, experiencing self-pity for not having a companion; this is often associated with hope. Ironically, people become closest to others by accepting that they are alone. The experience of isolation is most acute when people do not accept the essential separateness of each individual. Aloneness involves self-reliance, acceptance and faith; loneliness arises with field dependence, non-acceptance and hope.

Rebellion <--> Standing Forth

We discussed the distinction between standing out and standing forth in Chapter 2. Rebellion is another term worth considering. Rebellion occurs when one acts against a situation or another person; there is defiance and field dependency associated with rebellion. In this reaction against something or somebody, one becomes tied and dependent upon that something or somebody. With rebellion or revolution, individuality and independence are attained; these are issues of power and control.

Standing forth occurs when one firmly asserts oneself. This is not done against anyone else; rather, it is an expression of oneself, quite independent of anyone else. This is a process of self-affirmation and growth, which provides for the development of autonomy and individuation.

Submission <--> Surrender

These terms can be confusing in relation to sexuality, though they are also involved in nonsexual interactions. People often believe that love can be expressed in its highest form through the act of letting go with another; yet, they have also been warned against being dominated by somebody else for fear of losing their own identity. This dilemma can be untangled through an understanding of the difference between surrender and submission.

The act of submission is related to power. One person gives over control to someone else, yielding to the will of another. The main referent is the other; the self is diminished in importance. However, as in all power circumstances, both the one who dominates and the one who submits are invested in controlling the other, albeit from seemingly opposite ends of the pole. In existential terms, the exciting charge that is experienced over the prospect of submission is related to the flirtation with nonexistence or death – the giving up (or the taking over) of all responsibility through the ultimate dissolution of the will.

The act of surrender is related to giving up of control of the self, and its referent is only to the self, not to another. One surrenders (lets go) of oneself, but not to anyone else. In order to participate and be rewarded in society, people are encouraged to develop self-control through roles, social conventions and task competency. Such self-restraint is important to the development of one's personality; but at the same time it inhibits spontaneity and involves some loss of sense of oneself. The act of giving up such controls (as in surrender) results in a softening, an exhilaration, a sense of experiencing oneself again, fresh and new. This is the spirit of D.H. Lawrence's words in Aaron's Rod: "Give thyself, but give thyself not away."[8]

All relationships involve a dance between submission and surrender of the people involved, with alternating development of personal strength (with surrender) and power (with submission/domination). The relative amounts of those experiences determine the nature of a relationship and the possibility for personal growth within it.

Sentimentalism <--> Genuine Feeling

Oscar Wilde defined sentimentalism as "having the luxury of an emotion without paying for it."[9] We agree that sentimentalism is in this sense an indulgence. In sentimentalism, people experience feeling – not only the feelings of others but also their own – at a remove. In this mode, feeling is to some extent a form of entertainment, from which a person may derive pleasure or other stimulation. Indeed, the entertainment industry and mass media rely to a very large extent on the human capacity for sentimentalism. However, beneath this sometimes addictive attachment to sentimentality, there is frequently a desire for a more real and more direct experience of feeling. In developing strength, it is possible for individuals to experience their feelings more genuinely, as real time responses to actual people and current circumstances. As Oscar Wilde suggests, there may be a price to pay in opening to such feelings; there are also great rewards. In opening to deeper levels of feeling, and sharing these with others, people can experience their humanity more fully and discover the satisfaction of more intimate relationships.

Charge <--> Fulfilment

With strength, one feels an inner sense of fulfilment that is personally nutritive. In power orientations, one experiences a charge that is driven and stressful. In strength, one is in touch with one's deeper nature in a relaxed, certain way; one is bathed in the feeling of connection with oneself, and the rest of life. In power, the driven quality of striving to achieve the Ideal Self is fraught with tension, uncertainty, and anxiety; this can be very stimulating, but not usually relaxing!

Trust Others <--> Trust Self

In power orientations, one puts trust in others; since in this orientation trust involves expectation and control, one can then blame others when they do not do what one wants. In strength, one trusts oneself and has faith in one's own abilities to discriminate, respond and make choices.

Admiration <--> Inspiration

In admiration, people elevate those they admire, while reducing themselves; clearly, this is a power-based perspective. When people are aware of another, they can come into a fuller sense of themselves, their own potential, and their capabilities – this is being inspired.

Pride <--> Humility

Pride involves an inflated sense of self, and is a condition of non-being. Humility, a being state, involves a sensitive appreciation of oneself and of one's place in the world; humble individuals see themselves as significant but without exaggerating their importance. False humility is a power orientation where one sees oneself as lowly and insignificant; this involves a posturing, an unawareness of the uniqueness of the individual, and is a position of non-being.

Cynicism <--> Irony

Cynicism involves a devaluing of experience and a stepping back from life. The contempt for life in cynicism is self-defeating and involves pride and presumption (as if the cynic actually knows what is best, looking down on the world). Cynicism often accompanies the lack of courage to face life as it is. The contemptuous cynic disapproves of life rather than entering it.

Irony involves a very intimate appreciation and acceptance of life. Irony is involved in a very high form of humour, which acknowledges life as it is, while having a laugh at it. There is humility associated with irony (contrasted with the pride associated with cynicism).

Sacred <--> Holy

The word "sacred" is often used to describe situations that have been elevated to the status of special, important, honoured, inviolate, separate, and better. The term implies a morality, which elevates what is sacred; people make "sacred ground" and "sacred cows," and then do battle to conserve them. In this way, to make something sacred is to separate that item from the rest of life.

For us, the notion of "holy" involves a joining to life. When experiencing something holy, a person participates in a responsive manner. To appreciate each circumstance as connected to all of life is to have an holistic (Greek, *holos*, meaning "whole") viewpoint and a participation in the holy. People experience the holy aspect of any situation when they recognize its relationship to the rest of life. Unlike the sacred, there is nothing special about the holy; in every situation, even the commonplace, one can participate in the holy.

> "*The wretchedness of our world is grounded in its resistance to the entrance of the holy into lived life.*" – Martin Buber[10]

Perfection <--> Excellence

Perfection is related to the Ideal Self, and involves striving, achievement, and denial of the Authentic Self. Seeking perfection is associated with self-hate and dissatisfaction with life. Thus, the orientation of seeking perfection is related to non-being.

Excellence is a function of the Authentic Self and is related to mastery. Excellence involves an acceptance of life – not a striving for perfection, but rather a standing forth in expressing one's unique potential. Excellence comes with self-realization and self-expression. It is an attribute of being. Excellence is not the same as perfection (an impossible ideal); excellence implies a full expression of oneself.

On the next two pages we list the distinctions discussed in this and the previous chapter. Each term is also listed in the Index, starting on page 231.

In Chapter 2 Standing out	<-->	Standing forth
Control	<-->	Vulnerability
Non-being	<-->	Being
Isolation	<-->	Intimacy
Objectification	<-->	Being personal
Achievement	<-->	Mastery
Seriousness	<-->	Humour
Attention	<-->	Recognition
Security	<-->	Insecurity
Field dependency	<-->	Autonomy
Independence	<-->	Autonomy
Field dependency	<-->	Field awareness
Individualize	<-->	Individuate
Taking care of others	<-->	Caring about others
Sympathy/pity	<-->	Empathy
Victimhood and blame	<-->	Self-responsibility
Selfish	<-->	Self-centred
Self-hatred	<-->	Self-compassion
In Chapter 3 Minimize pain, maximize pleasure	<-->	Accept pleasure and pain
Political	<-->	Personal
Morality	<-->	Personal or situation ethics
Black/white thinking	<-->	Shades of grey
Guilt	<-->	Shame
Sensitivity to being hurt	<-->	Sensitivity to others
Shoulds/injunctions	<-->	Desires/choice
Obligations	<-->	Responsibility
Blame	<-->	Acceptance
Being to blame	<-->	Being responsible
Walls	<-->	Boundaries
Absence	<-->	Presence

Roles	<-->	Authenticity
Reaction	<-->	Response
Hope	<-->	Faith
Loneliness/isolation	<-->	Aloneness
Rebellion	<-->	Standing forth
Submission	<-->	Surrender
Sentimentalism	<-->	Genuine feeling
Charge	<-->	Fulfilment
Trust others	<-->	Trust self
Admiration	<-->	Inspiration
Pride	<-->	Humility
Cynicism	<-->	Irony
Sacred	<-->	Holy
Perfection	<-->	Excellence

4 Self-Esteem, Mirroring and Self-Compassion 自我同情.

Self-esteem is the measure by which people regard themselves, the value that they place upon themselves, the respect that they have for themselves. In recent years, the pursuit of high self-esteem has become a goal for many, which we believe has caused its own problems. In our own work we have paid more attention to self-compassion than self-esteem, for reasons we explain in this chapter.

Commonly, the development of self-esteem is seen to be related to the mirroring function in personality development. The simplistic idea is that the more value that children see reflected in their parents' eyes, the more they will value themselves; the more positive experiences that children have during their earlier years of development, the greater their possibility of developing high self-esteem. Consequently, parents and educators have been encouraged to build up children's self-esteem by giving them plenty of positive feedback and praise.

Our experience, however, is that people seem often to suffer from low self-esteem even when they are, by society's standards, very successful and receive a great deal of positive feedback. Often it appears to be that very sense of low self-esteem that accounts for the drive toward success. At the same time, we have encountered people who received very little positive mirroring as children and yet appear to have developed a solidly appreciative sense of themselves.

Most worrying to us is our observation that many people are striving for an idealized state of high self-esteem and in the process setting themselves up for failure and entrapment in the cycle of self-hate we described in Chapter 1. Some people seem even to believe that it was their right at birth to have been provided with the necessary environment (such as loving, highly regarding, mature parents) to engender high self-esteem. When this entitled expectation has not been met, people often feel resentment at having been betrayed and cheated by their parents. Some become fixated in the attitude that they are unlovable; they take the fact that their parents didn't seem to love them as proof of this.

In this chapter we want to take a closer look at this problem and develop a more nuanced understanding of the uses of mirroring and feedback. We propose that people do better when they experience honest, direct mirroring and feedback and learn to develop self-compassion than when they rely on positive attention to boost their sense of self-esteem.

The Development of Self-Evaluation: Mastery and Achievement

From very early in life, children experience, and frequently confuse, two different phenomena – the pleasure of mastery and the pride of achievement. They may experience a feeling of fulfilment and mastery when they take their first steps or learn to tie their own shoelaces or successfully maneuver food to their mouths. With mastery, children experience the intriguing rewards of discovery; they continue to feel pleasure as their world expands and they become increasingly more self-reliant and competent. In this way children can become more self-determining, motivated by an inherent desire to fulfil their potential, to actualize that which they yearn to realize, to express an inner drive to grow. In these circumstances, the best thing that a parent or teacher can do is to provide a safe learning environment and some encouraging support for such mastery to blossom and mature.

However, at the same time as having experiences of mastery, children also experience the pull to achievement and its rewards. As we saw in Chapter 1, children begin to recognize that what they do is always subject to evaluation, to judgments of good or bad, appropriate or inappropriate, satisfactory or unsatisfactory; furthermore, their behaviour seems to produce pleasure and displeasure in others. These circumstances foster field dependence in children; the evaluation of others becomes more important than the children's own pleasure of mastery. Thus achievement in pursuit of an Ideal Self often becomes the dominant aspect of a growing person's self-evaluation.

Mirroring: Learning to See Ourselves

Mirroring is the process through which caregivers provide feedback to growing youngsters. There are several types of mirroring; the most commonly experienced are concave and convex. Just as a concave mirror produces an image that is smaller than the original, psychological concave mirroring occurs with excessive criticisms that give the children the impression they are smaller than they are and less worthy in the parents' eyes. At the other end of the spectrum, a convex mirror produces an image that is bigger than the original; psychologically convex mirroring occurs when parents give excessive and unwarranted praise that make the child seem larger and more important than they are.

Through introjection, the child swallows whole the evaluating functions of the parents (creating what is variously called the Superego, the Parent Within, or the Ideal Self), and self-esteem becomes linked with this inner judging authority. The nature of this introjected authority (harsh, easy, inconsistent, or rigid) is closely related to the kind of mirroring provided to the child. Distortions in the mirroring function (such as over-valuing, or underestimating) can have a radical effect on the child's self-esteem.

If children are underestimated by their parents (that is, they receive concave mirroring), they will tend to introject an underestimating inner judge, resulting in beliefs of inadequacy, unworthiness, self-doubt, and uncertainty. These children grow to become self-effacing, uncertain adults who may be perfectionist but are never satisfied with themselves. The natural feelings of pleasure that come with mastery are abandoned in favour of such an evaluating process. Often this underlies the urgency to achieve the Ideal Self.

However, overvaluation by the authority figure rarely produces a happier situation. Such distorted (convex) mirroring may indeed produce within the child a superficial sense of high self-esteem; but if it does not match an inner sense of mastery, the child intuits it to be false. In such situations, children can develop contempt for the external authority (and then, by association, for all authority); frequently, this is accompanied by self-loathing for having duped those important authority figures and a desperate need to keep up the pretence. Thus, although parental overvaluation may appear to result in high self-esteem, it is accompanied by a deeper, more dangerous self-loathing and contempt for others. Frequently, these people become society's leaders and role models, whom the masses admire and wish to emulate – people like political leaders, movie idols, and rock stars.

Often children experience an unpredictable combination of concave and convex mirroring, and develop an unstable sense of self. If parents exhibit uncaring lack of concern, or inability to mirror at all, children will tend to see themselves as invisible, unworthy, and unlovable. Without mirroring of some sort, the psychological sense of presence that precedes self-esteem may atrophy, thus making any subsequent attempts at increasing self-esteem extremely difficult; such attempts may appear to be successful, but with a lack of true ground, the self-esteem generated may be fragile, hollow and unhealthy.

There is another style of mirroring, which we refer to as direct mirroring. In this style, parents give their children honest, considered, realistic feedback, based on what the parents' experience of their children really is. They are also interested to hear about their children's experience and perspective. Mirroring of this sort can help children develop a realistic, appreciative and accepting sense of who they are. Importantly, even when such mirroring was not readily available to people in their childhood, they can make it part of their adult experience and relationships. Such mirroring (both giving and receiving) is an important part of developing intimacy with others.

Seeking High Self-Esteem: A New Striving

High self-esteem has become a central goal for many therapists and educators. By making it an achievement that must be reached, they make self-esteem a new ideal. Such striving tends to reproduce the original problem of the self-hate cycle. By trying to achieve high self-esteem, people are hating themselves for not being perfect at acquiring self-esteem. In this process, they may attain a superficial sense of high self-esteem, only to discover more self-loathing and self-hate. They have made an icon of self-esteem, and miss it by trying to achieve it. This occurs in both students and their teachers; we have encountered many educators caught in the self-hate of believing they are not adequate teachers because they have not managed to bring forth high self-esteem in all their students!

We all would do well to devote more attention to developing self-compassion, self-acceptance, and self-love, as a means of experiencing a fuller sense of love with others. Then we could accept our level of self-esteem, low or high, without producing more disruptive self-hate.

Practicing the five A's we described in Chapter 1 (awareness, acknowledgement, acceptance, action and appreciation) is a most useful method to access increased self-compassion and find enhanced fulfilment in life.

5 Entitlement

I have taken forty years to make my psychology simple. I might make it still more simple.
I might say "all neurosis is vanity" – but this also might not be understood.
– Alfred Adler[1]

Entitlement is a natural occurrence in child development, in which infants believe that the world around them must provide for their wants or needs. Ideally, the maturation process involves a gradual relinquishing of this position. Although entitlement is important at the beginning, it can be very counterproductive if maintained later in life. The early phase of entitlement helps to establish a person's sense of importance in relation to the rest of the world. Later, this same "narcissistic" position often stands in the way of genuine dialogue with another and a mature perspective on one's place in society and the world. In our work we have seen many people who might be described as stuck in their entitlement phase; indeed, such fixation seems to us to be a characteristic phenomenon of our times. For reasons that will become clear in this chapter, we think it is crucially important for people urgently to address this issue.

Where Does Entitlement Come From?

In the womb, it seems that children experience a kind of union with their mothers and hardly distinguish themselves as separate. At birth, babies become physically separated; however, psychologically, children continue for some time to behave as if their mothers and the rest of the environment were part of them. As their perceptual functions develop, infants begin to make out vague outlines, and slowly come to identify one of these shapes as their regular provider (when they develop language, they will call this entity "Mother"). In the same manner, they learn to make out other people and objects. At the beginning, children treat all of these objects as extensions of themselves, not as separate entities. The project of psychological maturation involves distinguishing external objects and people, and assigning names to them. The development of language symbols provides a means for children to relate to the external world by labeling different parts of it.

Even when children gradually come to recognize that their mothers are separate from themselves, they still experience a sense of possessiveness. When they are hungry, their mothers are their servants, providing for their wants; when they are cold or wet, the people who are their possessions should cater to them. This is the experience of entitlement, which is a normal phase of early child development. Between one and two years of age, babies begin to move away from their parents physically, exploring the world around, constantly checking back to see that the parents are still pleased and under the child's control. As children move forward into the world, they carry with them a sense of entitlement. Just as they see their mothers as possessions, subject to their every whim and command, they apply this entitlement to the rest of the world, expecting attention and service.

Ideally, caregivers provide boundaries, and do not indulge a child's every whim. When children encounter these boundaries, they have an opportunity to develop an awareness that the parents are separate and distinct entities, with personal thoughts, feelings, and desires. Children will at first try to rebel against this awareness, attempting to bring parents under their control. If parents are successful in maintaining their own sense of boundaries, their children can continue to mature toward more distinct individuated selves. In the milieu of parental boundary-setting, done in an atmosphere of caring and consistency, children can begin to move from the narcissistic, self-involved world to acquire the capacity to recognize the personhood of another, and can begin to develop a more consistent and fulfilled sense of themselves. This long journey of acknowledging and respecting others' boundaries, and learning to define oneself in relation to others, is called the separation-individuation project.[2] We write in some detail about this object-relations view of child development in *The Illuminated Heart*.[3]

Parents can only stimulate development in their children to the degree that they have themselves developed; the task of parenting therefore includes with it an urgent call to "grow yourself up!" Unfortunately, parents often believe they are entitled to have their children be what they want (their idealized version of the child); such people have not learned to recognize genuine otherness and have little patience for the desires or differences of others. To the extent that parents fail to recognize the personhood of their children, they will likely reward their offspring with approval and attention to encourage the development of the Ideal Self. Children who are indulged in this way, who do not encounter parental boundaries or recognition, themselves fail to develop a sufficiently clear concept of the separate other. In their turn, these children maintain their entitled position as the centre of the universe. They grow up believing that the world owes them whatever they wish, and when their desires are not met, they see themselves as victims. They do not develop autonomous initiative, and are dependent upon others. As well, they do not learn the sensitivity to others that would help them experience greater object constancy, increasing subject constancy, and individuation.[4] Their psychological development arrests, and they remain fixated in their entitlement.

The Consequences of Entitlement

The consequences of remaining chronically stuck in entitlement are often dire, and the picture of entitlement we paint below is frankly grim. Sadly, the characteristics we outline are not uncommon. In fact, we think that very few people have negotiated the tricky process of growing up without becoming stuck to some degree or other in entitlement! Even the healthiest of us at times behave in some of the ways we describe below. The good news, we think, is that previously arrested issues can, with courage and insight, be revisited at any time, and stuck energy can be refound and remobilized.

Entitlement leads to people remaining like young children, irresponsible and without initiative. Expecting others to take care of them, entitled people make victims of themselves, feeling hurt and unhappy in their field dependence. They show limited empathy and much dependency upon others in relationships. They have little curiosity, and thus learn only what facilitates the acquisition of what they see as their due. Entitled people do not learn well from experience and develop little genuine interest or caring about others.

This disregard for others is manifested in such people's day-to-day interactions. For example, they might stand in a doorway, oblivious to anyone else who might want to go through. They will throw a cigarette butt onto the ground with no qualms about someone else having to pick it up; in their minds, other people are servants to indulge their carelessness. At a table, they will take the biggest and the best items of food without a thought for anyone else. They often show a lack of forethought, making emergency last-minute plans that inconvenience co-workers and friends. In relationships, they frequently think they are misunderstood when a partner does not agree with them; it is inconceivable to them that anyone else could have a valid point of view different than their own. When things do not work out the way they want, they react with blame or self-pity rather than self-investigation. Hence, personal responsibility is replaced by resentment of the world.

With entitlement there also comes a failure to develop courage. The entitled person operates from power and control rather than from the vulnerability and self-revelation that would facilitate the development of personal strength. Although outwardly confident, they often lack simple social skills and live with a chronic deep-seated fear for their own survival. With scant experience in developing boundaries, they instead construct walls that interfere with genuine dialogue. Deep down, they have a profound fear of intimacy; because they do not recognize others as real persons, they are suspicious and may have irrational fears of what others might do to them. Because they use walls rather than boundaries, they tend to be rigid, seeking clearly defined roles and expectations; thus, they are prone to adopt a herd mentality and are stifled in their creativity.

These same walls may render people more susceptible to what are sometimes called "boundary illnesses" such as asthma, allergies, and phobias. They may also be more prone to dependencies of all sorts – on institutions, on drugs, alcohol, TV, the internet, and on others who will support the illusion of their importance.

Often, their work is predominantly for security and financial gain, rather than for the sense of satisfaction that comes in collaborating with other humans in a sensitive dialogue of activity and love. They often experience a profound lack of rest and settling, because they have an incomplete sense of their location in life. With their inflated sense of self-importance, they are out of touch with their place. They are commonly involved in field-dependent attachments to the images of the Ideal Self, and less in touch with the Authentic Self; hence, they have considerable self-hate and self-denial.

Since this entitlement is so pervasive, it clearly has a detrimental effect on society as a whole. There is less cooperation, less consideration of others, more "me" and less "we." The spiritual values and sense of perspective that could arise from genuine dialogue with others do not develop. Ultimately, this has a global impact. It is increasingly clear, for example, that we cannot afford to continue believing ourselves entitled to exploit the resources of the planet without regard for the longer term or the needs of others. It is vitally important, therefore, that we "grow up" fast and learn to consider ourselves and others in a more mature, responsive and relational perspective. The entitled position is delusional and dangerous.

From Entitlement to Individuation, Curiosity, and Inclusion

It is possible for people to move beyond entitlements through awareness, acknowledgment, acceptance and choiceful action. The programs we designed at The Haven help people begin this process in the context of a group where honest feedback, curiosity, and intimate communication are taught and encouraged. People can take what they learn in such groups into their relationships with their families and friends, where they can continue step by step to let go their attachments to positions of entitlement. This takes courage, vulnerability, and determination.

We believe this is an honourable and vitally important path. People who are willing to relinquish entitlement become more responsible and experience more sense of themselves. They initiate rather than looking for others to begin things. The less entitled people are, the more they can pull their weight in a relationship. And as entitlement is relinquished, more advanced psychological functions begin to flourish: imagination, initiative, personal responsibility, and integrity are born from a self-reliant, unentitled position. In dialogue, such people will be more personal and will be genuinely interested in learning about others and themselves. When they are curious about themselves and each other, they can open up to a panoramic sweep of growth, embracing rather than defending against life and all its challenges. Such people are capable of true intimacy and inclusion, and can experience the self-fulfilment that comes with a thorough engagement with life. In this way, individuals can grow and develop, and stand forth to meet the tremendous challenges the world presents. There is so much evidence that human insensitivity is putting our very planet at risk that this has become a global imperative. It is ever more important that we find within ourselves the curiosity, will, and courage to walk this path.

Part II

In the Face of Anxiety

The greatest mystery is not that we have been flung at random among the profusion of the earth and the galaxy of the stars, but that in this prison we can fashion images of ourselves sufficiently powerful to deny our nothingness.

André Malraux[1]

6 **Existential Anxiety: The Challenge of Being Alive**

For life is at the start a chaos in which one is lost. The individual suspects this, but he is frightened at finding himself face to face with this terrible reality, and tries to cover it with a curtain of fantasy, where everything is clear. – José Ortega y Gasset[1]

The existentialist theologian Paul Tillich distinguished three types of anxiety "according to the three directions in which non-being threatens being." Anxiety, he suggested, appears in three forms:

> *The form of fate and death (briefly, the anxiety of death), that of emptiness and loss of meaning (briefly, the anxiety of meaninglessness), that of guilt and condemnation (briefly, the anxiety of condemnation). In all three forms anxiety is existential in the sense that it belongs to existence as such and not to an abnormal state of mind as in neurotic (and psychotic) anxiety.*[2]

Thus, the very state of being alive is accompanied by a chronic state of tension which Tillich refers to here as existential, and elsewhere as ontic, or ontological anxiety – that is, the anxiety of being in the face of non-being. This is a state peculiar to humans, who are capable of apprehending their own death; animals, as far as we know, do not experience such anxiety. As Rollo May put it, "animals have an environment, human beings have a world,"[3] and existential anxiety, with its terror of non-being, is a basic feature of that human world.[4]

In this way, the human state is accompanied by a deep sense of uneasiness. Humans are aware of their fragility and finitude, and experience profound, ontological anxiety in face of this. In an attempt to cope with this anxiety, each person develops a particular life-style. Such life-style patterning underlies the development of family, friends, culture, and the very fabric of society itself. In this sense, anxiety is a driving force of innovation, creativity, growth and change. However, when this life-style patterning does not adequately contend with the baseline anxiety, people become anxious in another way. They become anxious that what they are doing is not effectively inhibiting the basic, existential anxiety. In a cyclical fashion, such anxiety grows on itself and frequently becomes out of control and debilitating to the person. It is manifested in symptoms involving body, mind, and emotions; these are symptoms of neurotic anxiety. In extreme, as Tillich hints, this condition may devolve into psychotic anxiety.

People rarely have much direct experience of ontic anxiety; they quickly defend against it or convert it into neurotic anxiety. Neurotic anxiety is a reduced version of ontic anxiety, channelled into neurotic defences and patterns that people find easier to handle. Neurotic anxiety is involved in such neuroses as obsessions and compulsions, and underlies addictions and other self-destructive behaviours. Most people would rather have the symptoms of a neurosis than deal directly with the terror of being.

Ontic anxiety persists, however, as by its very nature it must. When people's defences are not sufficiently effective in distracting them from this root anxiety, they may experience isolation, meaninglessness, discontent, and profound doubts about the worth of their lives.

At such times, people question their purpose and goals. They may experience despair, or a sense of being lost or abandoned. They may lose sight of any reason to live, and some people may indeed choose to end their lives. Others, will revert to neurotic solutions they have used before, or find new ones, and continue to live severely limited, unhappy lives.

Nevertheless, it is possible to face up to the threat of non-being with courage and strength. In recognizing one's existential anxiety as a condition of being human, there is a challenge to face life courageously, to find personal meaning and self-compassion, and thus, the will to live. This belief has been at the heart of our work with people for the last 40 years, and we have a great deal to say in this book and elsewhere about how this can work in practice.

Not All Anxiety Is Pathological

Western traditional medicine has viewed anxiety as a symptom of an underlying disorder, or a cause of many psychosomatic illnesses, and so has devoted much attention to the eradication or suppression of anxiety. The view we have outlined above, on the other hand, sees anxiety as a basic phenomenon of life, underlying all change, growth, evolution, and socio-cultural achievements. From this point of view, not all anxiety is pathological. Indeed, anxiety is a condition of existence, and without it, we would not be alive and human.

Frequently, because the differences between forms of anxiety are not easily appreciated, both individuals and the medical profession tend to treat all anxiety alike. Through the indiscriminate use of anti-anxiety medication prescribed by a doctor, or the use of socially accepted drugs such as nicotine or alcohol, people attempt to alleviate or "cure" the anxiety state. Marijuana and cocaine, for example, are used both for pleasure and for relief of anxiety. When people have a low frustration-tolerance, they are unwilling to experience more than a slight level of pain, physically or emotionally. Drugs help to relieve the symptoms without addressing the underlying causes. At the same time, they contribute to a blunting of life's experiences, a levelling of the human condition to one of sedation and mediocrity.

In this way, we run the risk of creating peace without progress, tranquillity without a sense of meaning. This dilemma is dramatically encapsulated in the play *Equus* by Peter Shaffer, in which a psychiatrist struggles with the moral implications of numbing therapeutic intervention: "My desire," he says, "might be to make this boy an ardent husband – a caring citizen – a worshipper of abstract and unifying God. My achievement, however, is more likely to make a ghost!"[5]

Fear and Excitement

A useful distinction to think about in this context is between fear and excitement. The physiological responses we call fear and excitement are similar to one another, perhaps even identical. The heart rate quickens, breathing is increased, the skin perspires and perhaps develops "goose-pimples," the hair seems to lift, the pupils of the eyes enlarge. These symptoms of the "fight or flight" reaction are the same, whether the person is in danger of being beaten up or is experiencing an imminent possibility of winning millions of dollars in a lottery!

The only difference between such experiences is the person's interpretation of the situation. With excitement the person wants to be present in the experience (as in a roller-coaster); when the person has not freely chosen to be there, and danger is threatening, the person interprets the experience as fear and will want to get away from the situation. Frequently (but not always) people believe that safety has been provided in exciting situations; where they interpret that safety is lacking, they commonly will interpret their feeling as fear instead of excitement.

Similarly, the perspective we offer here on anxiety can be very useful. So long as people think of all anxiety as a problem to be feared and avoided, they will continue to medicate and numb themselves to avoid it. On the other hand, when people interpret anxiety as a basic condition of life that holds within it the potential for creativity and the discovery of meaning, they may find that there are occasions when they are prepared to embrace it! Of course, in this case there can be no guarantee of safety (it cannot be guaranteed even on the roller-coaster), but there is the possibility of a growing faith; and in realizing that this experience is common to all people, we can take heart and courage in the creation of honest, vulnerable relationships with one another.

Finding Your Bearings

Humans have developed a variety of standard meanings, activities, and goals to ameliorate, mask, and cope with the dread of nothingness, the meaninglessness of life. It is vital that people develop some of these basic skills in order to survive and flourish in the world. At birth, the child's experience of the world must be confusing and anxiety provoking: how can sense be made of such chaos? The growing child begins to organize reality through various "intelligences" – including linguistic, logical-mathematical, musical, temporal, spatial, bodily-kinesthetic, and personal – and by utilizing information provided by parents and others.[6] In this way children gradually develop a sense of themselves in relationship to the rest of the world. This sense of location, of finding one's bearings, provides a grounding that helps people deal with the underlying ontic anxiety. The more these intelligences are developed, the more solid one will feel. As we have seen, it is often when these methods become ineffective that people develop what we have called neurotic reactions to anxiety. Extreme loss of these intelligences is often considered symptomatic of mental illness; relative losses may result in a state of confusion in which people experience difficulty in making sense of life. In the next chapter we discuss how people must locate themselves in time and space, and some of the problems that can arise in this attempt.

Obsessing: An Everyday Neurosis

Obsessing is an example of how people use neurotic anxiety to cover over existential anxiety. An obsession is a repetitious thought that is difficult to relinquish. A compulsion is a repetitious activity that is dictated by the obsession; the obsession is the thought, and the compulsion is the action that is linked with the obsession. People become obsessed as a way of coping with basic, ontic anxiety. They fill their minds with the same repetitious (and thus, dependable and secure) thoughts; their actions, dictated by the obsessions, are therefore also predictable. By this means, people achieve a measure of security; their life becomes predictable amidst the inevitable chaos.

It is possible to see most of human life as involved in obsessions and compulsions. People spend a great deal of time in obsessive thought patterns and get into obsessive-compulsive relationships, and compulsive patterns related to their home and work life. We have written about this in *Joining: The Relationship Garden*, proposing that people acknowledge their obsessions to an intimate partner, and work their way to more freedom by revealing to one another their repetitive thought processes and the actions that habitually follow them. To become more free from obsessions can be double-edged; people who accomplish this find more energy and creative ideas, but with an accompanying increase in anxiety and uncertainty. The five A's we outlined in Chapter 1 are a helpful way to do this, encouraging self-compassion in this vulnerable and sometimes difficult process.

Embracing Ontic Anxiety

When individuals begin to come to terms with ontic anxiety, by learning to acknowledge and accept rather than repress it, their interactions can become less dependent and relieved of the desperate need to control. Then relationships can be characterized more by a sharing of two autonomous solitudes than a melding of two individuals into one. Then two people can become more, rather than less, of themselves in dialogue! The relationship becomes like a garden, in which each individual thrives, relating to others by free choice.

Unfortunately, most relationships are more like a trap, in which each person becomes contracted, attached to the other by fear. When people are autonomous, they deal with their ontic anxiety constructively; when people are dependent, the ontic anxiety is covered over and ignored. Both relationship styles are means of coping with ontic anxiety. Intimate relationships can provide a sense of satisfaction that helps people deal successfully with ontic anxiety. Without satisfying relationships, individuals frequently experience a sense of loneliness that, in the extreme, becomes a feeling of isolation. The less the degree of intimacy, the more likely that people will revert to control methods to compensate.

It takes courage to start facing up to the facts of life and death, or being and non-being, and to reveal one's anxiety to another. When people devote themselves to avoiding these facts, to defending with all their might against ontic anxiety, they also miss the enormous creative potential and strength that is held within it.

Many men never give out the whole of themselves, their deepest truth. They live on the surface, and yet, so rich is the soil of humanity that even this thin outer layer is able to yield a kind of meagre harvest which gives the illusion of real living ... how many men will never have the least idea of what is meant by supernatural heroism, without which there can be no inner life! Yet by that very same inner life shall they be judged ... Therefore when death has bereft them of all the artificial props with which society provides such people, they will find themselves as they really are, as they were without even knowing it – horrible undeveloped monsters, the stumps of men. – Georges Bernanos[7]

Our own experience, and that of many others, has been that it is worth the risk to look squarely at and embrace the anxiety that is a condition of our being human.

When you walk to the edge of all the light you have and take the step into the darkness of the unknown, you must believe one of two things will happen – there will be something solid for you to stand on, or you will be taught to fly. – Patrick Overton[8]

7 Location: Finding Freedom in Time and Space

Time

The past is a treacherous whore
*   entrapping us in the pain of*
regrets and lost desires
The future is a romantic boy
*   lost in the dreamy landscape*
of vague imaginings
The present is the living glory
*   of senses, feelings and affections*
alive in wonder and grace

We must find
*   brave new words*
sturdy language
to break free
*   from the shackles*
of mindbound conventions
and habituated vision

to express ourselves
*   without romanticism*
without sentimentalism
without cynicism
without hope

and especially
*   without regret*

— Jock McKeen, 1998.

In this chapter we discuss ways in which people try to cope with the challenges presented by time and space in their lives. Most people are to some degree or other stuck in particular, fixated relationships either with the past or the future, and consequently have a hard time responding fully to events and people in the present. Similarly, people often have difficulty locating themselves flexibly between their inner and outer worlds and in relation to things and people in their lives. It is essential for basic functioning in life that people learn to locate themselves in space and time, and yet often in the process they severely limit the possibilities of their lives. In this chapter we take a closer look at some of the ways people become stuck and consider some options for finding more flexibility and autonomy.

A Place to Start: Primary Contextual Location

At birth, a child's major challenge is to face chaos and attempt to organize it. In order to survive in an unpredictable world, children must learn to identify all the objects (including people) that come into the sphere of their senses of touch, sight, sound, smell, and taste. Depending on how pleasant or unpleasant their experiences prove to be, they gradually build up memories of where they wish to be in relationship to these objects. By doing so, they begin to make sense of their surroundings and become increasingly capable of identifying their location in relation to those objects. In the presence of a caring environment, children experience that they are wanted, and tend to locate themselves as desired objects in the world. When experiences are mostly negative, they will locate themselves as undesirable and readily abandoned objects in the world. This is the nature of their primary contextual location, which will set the emotional tone for the life-journey upon which each newborn embarks. The primary contextual location is the starting place for the palette of affective colours (for example, sombre and serious, or bright and joyful) that an individual will tend to develop in undertaking life's tasks. These early experiences play an important part in influencing which emotions a person will typically feel throughout life. The range of these can potentially be enhanced later, although it is important to recognize the impact of this primary location.

Within their primary contextual location, infants face the world and its opportunities in at least two distinct dimensions, namely time and space.

Location in Time

As the infant develops, he or she slowly begins to appreciate the recurrent nature of events. For example, when mother disappears from view, she will probably return (sometime in the "future"). At certain times food will appear, ideally closely following hunger pangs. Such regular activity provides the basis for faith within the developing person, and trust of caregivers. Through experience and memory, children begin to locate themselves in relation to the events along their personal time continuum.

Later, they will be able to compare their location in time with that of others; but this comparison will make sense only when they are able to locate themselves on their own time lines.

Generally, people grow up with a more or less stable and functional orientation in time. However, in moments of stress or anxiety they are in varying degrees prone to lose this stability. Adults frequently regress, and react in the present as if they were facing past circumstances; these reactions and behaviours may have been effective in the past but are inappropriate to the present time. This is commonly experienced, for example, by people who remember abuse in their past. In the face of threatening situations, such people quickly revert to attitudes and behaviours of helplessness from childhood, often with feelings of fear; usual solutions include running away, hiding, withdrawing, blaming, and becoming willful, resistant, indulgent, childishly hysterical, or rebellious. Such behaviours may have been useful in the past, or even saved the child's life; however if they become fixated in time and compulsively repeated, there is unlikely to be any movement toward a new solution that could open up the person's world and promote healthy growth. People who do this are often desperately trying to stop time, to resist change and experience less, so that their world might become more manageable. As they learn to locate themselves more solidly in the present, they often learn to experience themselves more expansively, using a growing curiosity to open more to change. They develop an increasing trust in themselves and others, and a sense of faith.

THE DOCKS: GETTING STUCK AND LEARNING TO LET GO

Events in our past often play an enormous part in our lives today. Most of us will quickly regress when faced with traumatic or risky circumstances in the present. This can be quite dramatic; we hear an angry voice in the street, for example, and it is suddenly as if we are back in our childhood, terrified by a violent father. We all have these fixated positions in our past, usually identified with an earlier age at which we experienced some very significant events – frightening, enjoyable, or both. Because we so readily visit these past events, we sometimes have great difficulty responding appropriately or effectively to events and people in the present.

Many participants in our programs have found the following simile useful. It describes a process that for most people happens quite unconsciously. By becoming aware of the process, people can address how they wish to respond. Life is like a voyage on a river; the passing of time is marked by events, which can be seen as docks that one's boat passes by. Sometimes we tie our boat to one of these docks for a while, experience what is there to experience, and then move on freely. On other occasions, however, people are reluctant to leave a dock that seems to hold a particular fascination for them (either because the experience is a great pleasure or a great horror). But leave them they must, because the river of time flows on: they set off again in their boat... but omit to untie their mooring. Instead, they leave a long rope attached to the dock as they continue on. Attached in this way, they become fixated in their location in time, although they continue their journey down the river. When faced with charged, anxiety-provoking experiences later in their journey, they tend to "snap back" to the dock in the past; it is as though the ropes were elastic, like bungee cords! Because people so often return to old docks, they become limited in their ability to assess or appreciate the new docks in the present. The return to old docks seems to occur automatically, and for most people, this is just how life is.

It is possible however, to involve oneself more deeply in this process, take responsibility for it, and consider different choices. People can come to see how their fixation on certain "docks" of history keeps their lives limited, restricting their capacity to travel to other locations in their land-scapes. Though the experience of "snapping back" to the past can be very vivid, happening in an instant as if we had no control, people can consider that they are in fact pulling on the ropes themselves in order to return to the docks in the past. They can ask themselves: "What am I getting out of holding on to this dock with such determination?" or "What awful thing would happen if I let go of this experience?" And they can recognize that they have choices to make: do they wish to carry on pulling themselves back to the docks or will they learn how to let go of the ropes to the past and respond to what is happening here and now?

LIMITING THE ANXIETY OF THE PRESENT

People who resist time refuse to change their manners or morals in rela-tion to the present. They wish to keep their lives manageable by not having to relate to changing events; they yearn for the familiar past. Sometimes that past contains traumatic or unpleasant experiences that continue to govern their present; for example, people who have been sexually assaulted in the past often relate to men or women in the present (depending on the gender of the original abuser) as though they all are going to be exploitative, thus limiting their relationships. In this way, people attempt to manage anxiety; they do so at the cost of narrowing their world and limiting their relationships. This kind of fixation on the past (frequently accompanied by a tendency to psychologically leave the body, or to hate the body and its sensations) arose originally as a means of survival; however unpleasant the effects might be, it continues as a means of making the present more manageable. To do otherwise would mean having to assess and respond to each new event and acquaintance in the present. This would take awareness and courage; and it could bring with it significant rewards.

Location in Space

As well as locating themselves in time, people must also locate themselves along a space continuum. Each person is suspended between "inner" and "outer" space. As they grow up, children learn in differing degrees to abandon their inner experiences in order to concentrate on the myriad tasks in external space that are essential to survival (for example, walking, talking, reading, self-care, social niceties and consideration). Between the interior space the child knows, and the external space that is unfamiliar lies the "transitional space," a region of relative familiarity between the two. It is in this transitional space that children meet (and learn how to control) significant other people in their lives. Individuals do not locate themselves only in relationship either to themselves or others. Rather, all people locate themselves somewhere along this space continuum. In so doing, they become more or less self-reliant or field dependent. This occurs in varying (but usually characteristic) degrees. Each individual establishes a characteristic stance in life with regard to space and time, becoming more or less comfortable with inner and outer worlds, as well as past and present time.

Our educational institutions tend to support a reliance upon outer experiences and other people, with a relative abandonment (and often suspicion) of inner space. People are encouraged to concentrate on controlling their environment and the people in it; they learn to please, to manipulate, to dominate, to be nice, to display only socially acceptable feelings and behaviour. The better they do it, the more acceptance they earn. Those who are adept at this project become comfortable, living much of their time in relation to great numbers of people, and in a great variety of spaces. However, this comes at a considerable cost, as people lose a sense of solid location within themselves.

LIMITING THE ANXIETY OF SPACE

As we saw in Chapter 6, there are so-called neurotic solutions to ontic anxiety. Such solutions can be seen in relation to our location in space. People who are uncomfortable with large, unknown, and uncontrollable spaces react with nervousness; they experience being threatened and uncomfortable. The most direct and undefended form of the inability (or the perceived inability) to handle much space occurs in the syndrome known as agoraphobia (the fear of open spaces). Even though most people's reactions are usually less extreme, many still relate to the spatial domain with a variety of defensive behaviours and symptoms. These conditions often are given labels by medical practitioners; but for the people suffering them, the experiences are very compelling and frequently disturbing. The label from outside is an aid for the practitioner to offer some relief; but for the individuals in the situation, there are many feelings and torments that are profoundly unsettling. For example, so-called boundary illnesses such as allergies and phobias (see Chapter 13) can serve to control the anxiety or the threatening environment by limiting the scope of one's activity. In a similar fashion, the obsessions and compulsions of everyday life often serve to organize people's environment and attention to such a degree that they might never encounter their underlying anxiety. When these defences are extreme, people's lives become handicapped by the necessity to perform repetitious rituals or behaviours (such as addictions to substances or people, compulsive work, repetitive self-destructive actions, or unrelenting repetitious thoughts). When these patterns become debilitating, they are often diagnosed as neurotic illnesses.

The cost of managing anxiety in these ways is that, in order to make their world more manageable, people make it smaller. Choices become limited, freedom is curtailed, and the mind is relieved of any need to face the root problems. Furthermore, if people become medically sick, they may expect others to take over much of the responsibility for their lives. Others will make decisions for them, will supply endless attention, and will support the view that they are helpless victims of families, friends and society. This process has a significant and sometimes dire impact on the quality of individual lives and on society as a whole.

In neurotic solutions to the experience of anxiety, people become fixated somewhere in the intersection of space and time, losing the freedom to move freely along these axes. They have made their world smaller and thus more manageable, although much less expressive of the vastness of their authentic being. Their present becomes contaminated by the past, and their inner space has less expression in outer space.

Remarkably, a great number of people locate themselves through their suffering. Chronic physical pain or emotional distress, although very uncomfortable, can be quite predictable. Hence, in an ironic fashion, these people can locate themselves, and achieve some measure of security by having symptoms of illness, or some other form of suffering. Their ontic anxiety is obscured by their ongoing relationship with pain or other symptoms. Closely related to this is guilt, a form of emotional pain; some people (or cultures) locate themselves and find security in chronic guilt, and indeed, guilt can become an integral part of their identity.

Psychotic Solutions

If people find outer space and the experience of the present too dangerous, they can dedicate their everyday behaviour to obsessions, compulsions, and addictions. Instead of developing contactable, sensitive boundaries, these people tend to construct isolating, thick, defensive walls. Behind these walls is the experience of safety; nevertheless, these people are inwardly helpless, fixated in a different time and place, unable to deal adequately with the present. In the extreme, they might ignore reality entirely; this is what happens in psychotic episodes.

This can occur if the neurotic solution still does not adequately handle the anxiety; then, people might remove themselves even further from others and the threatening circumstances in the environment, by withdrawing further into their inner worlds. They occupy much smaller spaces. Although for some the experience is one of abject terror and powerlessness, for many, this psychotic withdrawal provides an arena in which they have an experience of greater control, where they are the unchallenged authorities. They become out of touch with others by becoming emotionally numb, unaffected by the exigencies of a normal life, which seem too much to bear. Because they are masters of that inner space, all seems possible; they can experience themselves as either more powerful or more helpless, unrelated to the measurements of reality. From their vantage point, they are safe; in conventional society, they are pathologically out of touch, and may well be diagnosed as psychotic.

Medicating Anxiety

Currently, it is common practice to treat neurotic and psychotic reactions to anxiety with prescription drugs. Although these pharmacological agents are useful in allaying the anxiety, they do not in themselves address the underlying problems stemming from fixations in space and time. Indeed, these drugs may reinforce people's sense of helplessness and encourage development of an addiction to being helped. The individual experiences a loss of faith in inner space, and an increasing need to trust authorities in outer (transitional) space; at the same time, these authorities are commonly hated and feared. It is amidst these kind of ambivalent love-hate relationships that people experience being trapped in both time and space, living a life of restricted pleasure and meaning.

We are not against drugs to assist in the treatment of symptoms. Often, they can serve as useful aids to support individuals' struggles to take charge of their inner world. Sometimes staying on a regular medication is a practical solution to bring regularity and calm. The underlying challenge, whether aided or not by medication, is to come to terms with and manage one's own anxiety, and so remain solidly located in time and space. Each situation is individual and personal.

Finding Freedom in Time and Space

People orient themselves somewhere in the intersection of the continuum of space and the line of time. Healthy, mature individuals (who are rare) would be able to move freely along both of these planes, changing as appropriate to each situation. Such people could play like a six-year-old child with six-year-old children by choosing to regress in time, to really express the energy of the six-year-old within. During play, these persons would freely move from inner space, where fantasies and emotions are abundantly available, to express them in outer space, where they could be shared with playmates. At the end of playtime, such persons could readily come into the present as adults, in order to organize the toys and clean up the mess in the room (outer space) in which the fairies and dragons of inner space had played; they might even prepare for the future by storing the toys in readiness for the next episode of play. Their present has reference to memories of the past, and anticipation of the future, without being fixated.

In order to break away from crippling fixations in time and space, individuals need courage to remain present and in touch. This is easier in an understanding, supportive environment, where they can learn to travel more freely along the time/space axes. In order to affirm themselves, people must directly address the fears that trigger the spontaneous flashbacks to past time and space, and develop the strength to remain vulnerable and in contact with others. If people are to find the safe harbour within themselves, they must learn how to let go of past fixations that have been used to anchor themselves in the caretaking ports of others.

We close this chapter with one of Ben's teaching stories that addresses the topics we've discussed here in a form that many people have found illuminating.

The Landscape of Our Lives

By Bennet Wong

I have found that people tend to be goal-directed. They frequently wish to fix some problems in their lives, to let go of unfortunate situations, to forget unhappy relationships, to finally deal with their feelings about the past, to be able to face the future changed and unimpeded. After devoting much time and money with counsellors and other people helpers, they are often astonished to discover their demons to still be with them. For myself, I now have arrived at the belief that nothing will ever be done with, that we will never be rid of the past, and that ultimately, the essentials about ourselves will never change!

I have shifted from a belief that human experience is a linear affair from past to present to future, to a belief that each of our lives is an immutable landscape of experience. We all have our mountains of exhilaration, surrounded by our cliffs of danger and hardships. Each of us has places of contentment and placidity, like soothing lakes and gentle forests; similarly, each has deep, exciting and sometimes threatening waters as well as scary, unknown jungles. There are in everyone various parched deserts and lush, productive wetlands. Each landscape is endless in the variety of appearances and experiences.

Although the choices are numerous, most people tend to limit themselves to living in only a few parts of the total possibilities. Some people are mountain people while others tend to live in their valleys. However, no matter which part of their landscape that they may find themselves, if they would look carefully in all directions, they would see that the entire landscape is always there, but some parts are in the background. What they are experiencing has only moved into the foreground. Nothing has been exterminated or altered. All that has changed has been the location of the present experience.

So, when experiencing happiness, a person should be aware that somewhere in the background still lurks an area of sadness. While experiencing joy in the foreground, despair has only been relegated to the background at that time. Some people become fixated to one location; even when they are in safe and happy circumstances, they are unable to shift the dangerous, harmful childhood experiences from their foreground into the background. Thus, such a person is anxious and depressed even when the current context would provide ideal circumstances for security and pleasure. By remaining stuck in one area of the landscape, this person has diminished the scope of experience; the landscape has become a small window of the whole larger picture. Such a narrowing and fixation is what accounts for neurosis.

If this metaphor of life is understood, it would seem that to ensure good mental health, people should be encouraged to visit all parts of their landscape to remain aware of the wide range of possibilities of experience. If they are able to remain flexible to shift readily, not having to remain rigidly in one place (as occurs in a fixed moral position), they will be able to stay attuned to present circumstances. That would be a sign of good mental health.

Such a metaphor begs the consideration of another set of dynamics. What if the person were unable to sustain a portion of the landscape for a reasonable length of time? Such would be the case in people who experience sudden shifts and wide ranges of movement. Foreground and background are unable to remain stable. The person would experience severe dislocation, unable to have a stable sense of identification. They would be described by outside observers as being all over the map. The sustainability of foreground is another sign of good mental health.

Now that I have this picture of mental health, I no longer waste energy trying to fix anything. I now more focus on helping myself and other people to more easily move through our personal landscapes.

Now that you have read Ben's story, you can see how we frame our approach to personal growth and development, for ourselves, and for our clients and friends and family. Our task in life is to locate ourselves, where we are, here, now, in the midst of our current context.

8 **From Objectification to Inclusion: Bridging the Gap**

In this chapter, we examine the phenomenon of objectification. We start by exploring its origins in the normal developmental process of children and point out how useful and necessary it is for children to establish a secure place for themselves in the world and to manage the potentially overwhelming flood of anxiety provoked by the realization of one's own existence. Next, we look at some of the limiting and divisive consequences of becoming fixated in objectification. Finally we suggest ways in which it is possible to move beyond the limitations of objectification into more personal contact and dialogue with others.

From the outset we want to emphasize that objectification is perfectly normal, and necessary. Problems arise when people become fixated in objectification and know little or nothing else about themselves or how to relate with others.

Learning to Objectify: An Essential Task

When children are born, they separate physically from their mothers. However, this physical separation is not accompanied by an immediate psychological separation. It seems likely that the newborn child is experientially and psychologically largely undifferentiated from its entire environment; everything is in some ways an extension of the child. Because the perceptual apparatus has not yet developed, early experiences are ill defined and all-or-none in their scope. The child experiences global reactions to hunger or satiety, heat or cold, pain or pleasure, dark or light.

As perception improves, children gradually begin to make out gross shapes around them, and to attach labels to these shapes. They learn to distinguish one huge shape that comes and goes, seemingly associated with relief of distress; this shape they will ultimately call "Mother" or whatever name represents the primary caregiver, male or female. The first eighteen months of life are involved in rapid perceptual development and with it the identifying and naming of objects (including people). By this naming, children are symbolizing experience and organizing their perceptions into a reproducible reality. Through distinguishing and naming objects, processes which are necessary for their development, children learn to identify the world around them and begin to make sense of it, gradually establishing control over their surroundings.

Growing children move around in and play amidst this assemblage of objects. They make larger excursions away from their primary security objects, their mothers or those in the "mother" role. As children crawl away, they look back over their shoulders, to make sure that mother is still there. As they become more confident, they will even play in the next room, with periodic voice contact with their mothers. Thus, children assemble a picture of their mothers, known by object relations theorists as the "internal object."[1] As this object becomes more stabilized, youngsters learn to move in the world with the security of knowing that their parents (and the protection associated with parents) exist. In this way, the symbolization of others is an important method for psychological control and stability.

In the first two years, even as children are naming objects, it is likely that they still do not clearly distinguish the objects as separate from themselves. The "mother" that comes and goes is experienced as an extension of the child. The teddy bear that the child holds is still part of the child, not a separate entity. Indeed, children likely see all things that they name and objectify as part of themselves; this is the "primary narcissism" of the infantile state. Although they are distinguishing separate objects (and thus honing their faculties of discrimination), they still see the objects as themselves. So, in this view, children have a me-mother, a me-toy, and me-food.

Many theorists believe that the clear distinction of a "self" from the objects surrounding it only occurs between the ages of two and three, when self-awareness is established. It is in this period that the child recognizes, "I am here!" Thus, during the "terrible twos," children are experimenting with their self-directed wills and establishing a more stable experience of themselves; this culminates in the "birth" of the self at about age three. From this point on, the individual's will and personal choices come to the fore, and that individual is ready to embark upon a life of individuation. We note that not all theorists agree that the self-sense stabilizes at about age three. Some writers cite current research that supports a view that the self is present from the beginning. We ourselves agree with the notion that the self is a "pre-emergent potential" at birth; we assert that there is a being from the start, and the self is developed through experience.

The Limitations of Relating to Objects Rather Than Persons

As Becker described, parents are seen by their children as huge and powerful, protectors against the ravages of the universe.[2] Children experience feelings of security in having their parents on their side. However, the recognition slowly dawns that these parents, who are so powerful, could be a great threat to the children's well-being if ever they became displeased!

Thus, children are ambivalent about their caregivers – their parents, who are powerful enough to ward off the threats of the universe, could also use this same power to destroy their children.

Parents are larger than life, to be revered, appreciated, and feared. Thus, children learn to anticipate what the big people want, and devote themselves to the activities of pleasing in order to take control of the objectified parents. Of course, children are terrified of being abandoned, and want to assure themselves that they will not be left behind by their caregiver-objects. At first, this pleasing is quite primitive and impotent; the child learns to entice with crayon scribblings and peek-a-boo games. Very quickly, these activities become more sophisticated and are incorporated into a serious process of field-dependent pleasing, in which people quell their own desires in the face of the imagined demands of the external.

This is the process by which children establish the Ideal Self we discussed in Chapter 1, in an attempt to get control and establish security against anxiety and the threat of abandonment. In this way, youngsters sell out the fledgling Authentic Self. If children choose a pattern of control and manipulation to develop a walled self, they lose contact with the Authentic Self. Most children become arrested in a world of objects, and deny their own autonomy and self-development in exchange for the security of control over the objects in their environment. Most adults retain much of this infantile approach to relationships, at least in part, limiting their personal connection with others. Thus, little genuine dialogue occurs, since people do not learn to relate to the humanness of others.

This is the basis of what Martin Buber called the "I-It relationship," where people relate to one another primarily as objects rather than persons.[3] As we shall see, for an "I-You" relationship between real persons to flower, individuals would have to face the terror of non-being and accept aloneness and lack of control over external objects. Then, truly personal relationships would become possible.

We have much more to say about the process of becoming more personal in relationships with others, in this book and in *Joining: The Relationship Garden*. For now, we wish to point out that objectification underlies a great deal of sexual charge and attraction, which is frequently what brings people together in a relationship in the first place. This is another of objectification's many uses! However, as we explain in Chapter 9, sexual involvement is not the same as intimacy. Indeed, until people learn to personalize this basically impersonal force, sexuality can be an impediment to intimacy as we define it. We devote an entire chapter to this important topic in *Joining: The Relationship Garden*.

Enemy Making

The anxiety associated with the chaos of life seems unmanageable; hence people experience a need to organize and control the objects (and the objectified people) around them. By doing so, they create meaning; this involves deciding on "right" and "wrong," "good" and "bad," "appropriate" and "inappropriate." In this way, people create morality to govern the interactions between themselves and others. The purpose of such morality is to provide a continuity and security for the individual and the culture. Unfortunately, as Freud and others have pointed out, the importance ascribed to this morality tends to grow beyond this basic function; the guidelines of morality becoming rigidly codified and invested with meaning beyond their function. Morality becomes a method for objectifying people as the "other" or the enemy.[4]

Throughout history, millions of people have been killed in the service of cultures and moralities. The objectification of people (as "enemies," "infidels," or "barbarians") immediately robs them of their humanity; in war, the actual killing of the body is only a small further step, since the enemy has already been dehumanized. This is why military training devotes so much effort to teaching soldiers how to depersonalize the "foe." A person who is the father of children would find it difficult to kill another father; it is easier for a "soldier" to kill an "enemy," a "conqueror" to kill a "native," a "defender of the faith" to kill a "heretic."

People do the same in their everyday lives, objectifying others in order to control them, making enemies of them in the process. It is likely that there is another, perhaps deeper layer to this process. Because the chaos of people's inner world is closer to themselves, it is possibly even more frightening than the external. Many impulses and feelings that arise from within people (from the desire to be unkind to the urge to kill) are unacceptable to them. The convenient solution is to repress and deny such impulses, attempting to hide them in what Jung referred to as one's shadow. At the same time, people may project these shadow aspects of themselves outwards onto others, thus relieving the pressure of the inner world, though possibly making the outer world even more terrifying than before. Objects that are projected upon in this way become identified as the "enemy," or "wild" or "crazy." In addition to individuals, whole civilizations appear to need these objects of projection, even establishing permanent institutions to service them.

It is through objectifying processes of this sort that people create a gap, a separation, between themselves and others. Whatever is unknown is interpreted as a threat; in order to gain control over it, people objectify it and make an enemy of it. This is the manner in which many women and men, cultures and societies, religions and institutions view one another. In relationships, this is the process by which children and parents become alienated and partners become separated. The gaps are maintained by the establishment of morality; somebody always needs to be "right," making others "wrong." By sustaining the gaps, grudges are held and punishments required. To relinquish the gaps would mean giving up the convenience of having objects to project upon; then individuals would have to face the horror within, to contend with unacceptable impulses and feelings that well up from inner space, and ultimately to be responsible for themselves. In the same manner, institutions could become responsible, rather than blaming and persecuting other institutions or individuals. However, responsibility is quite uncommon. The magnitude of the fear and anxiety that accompany such responsibility explains why persons and institutions desperately cling to a rigid morality of rightness, making others wrong, instead of opting to let go of control and make happier living possible.

We developed programs at The Haven to help people become aware of aspects of themselves that they have projected onto other people and learn to accept them as aspects of their own shadow. Remarkably, in this learning process, people often find that in their striving for their Ideal Self they have repressed and denied not only the "bad stuff" but also aspects of their natures that they would now like to have a larger part in their lives, such as humour and joy! With this awareness, it becomes possible to reclaim and deal more responsibly with aspects of oneself that were previously disowned.

Disowning the Body

A similarly objectifying process also occurs internally, between the self and the body. Because the self is so identified with awareness and consciousness, it is often thought to be the mind itself, independent of the body. Because so much that occurs within the body is unconscious and uncontrollable, people often relegate the body to a position separate from themselves, and relate to the body as an object. Because their bodies are always with them, people can use them as handy screens upon which to project their anxieties, fears, anger, hate, and love. Thus, many make enemies of their bodies, disowning and distancing from them. The more alienated people are from their bodies, the more frightened and defended they become. The more split off from their bodies they become, the greater the distance they experience with others. Thus, the gap widens. In this separation from the body and from others, many illness processes can take root and grow, seemingly beyond the person's control, as we discuss in Part IV of this book.

Bridging the Gap: The Move Toward Dialogue

Thomas Szasz identified a human capacity to move through modes of conversation he described as autologue, monologue, and dialogue. He described thinking as self-conversation that occurs in the metaphorical space we call mind. As such, all thinking is related to language. Since such self-conversation (that is, thinking) is from the self to the self in the privacy of the mind, it is referred to as an autologue.[5]

Early on, children discover that the use of language is attention-getting and controlling. Besides using language to think (as in autologue), expressing what they are thinking reaps a harvest of attention from others. Through such expression, children announce their needs, so that expectations can be met from the "objects" (initially the caretakers) around them. Since young children lack an appreciation of the personhood of those others, their expressions take the form of a "monologue." The situation is very similar to an actor on stage, informing the audience about inner occurrences in a character, yet being unable to hear what is going on within the audience members. Most people fail to develop much beyond this level of communication, and so many interactions consist of mutual monologues. These conversations may offer the illusion of control, attention, even a simulacrum of relationship; but, people experience in them little or no genuine fulfilment or recognition.

The task of moving from a world of "objects" to discover others (and hence the self) as persons involves recognizing and acknowledging those others. To do so requires an interest in the other, and a consideration of the other as a unique, autonomous, self-determining, responsible being whose world of inner experiences can be felt and appreciated. Such is the nature of what Buber called inclusion, the "I-You" relationship. At such a time, there can be a mutual sharing of inner experiences – true dialogue. In this way is it possible for objectified beings to transform into real persons who live and feel their connection and their location in life; people can learn to "bridge the gap" of separation, which then fades into the background.

The I-You Relationship: Dialogue and Inclusion

The relationship becomes truly dialogical when both people become aware of the humanness of the other. This is the process of inclusion.

Inclusion... is a way of imagining the other in his unique wholeness in the most real way possible. This act involves conceiving what the other, the desired partner of the dialogue, is thinking, wishing, feeling and perceiving.[6]

In Martin Buber's terms, the relationship becomes one person relating to another as "I-You" rather than "I-It." In this dialogue, both parties are experienced as human and persons, not just as objects. In the I-You dialogue, Buber spoke of inclusion as "a bold swinging, demanding the most intensive stirring of one's being, into the life of the other."[7]

This is the kind of relationship that we, the authors, have developed in our life together. The communication model that we taught in Haven programs and outline in Chapter 10 is designed to help people move beyond autologue and monologue into true dialogue with another through a process of self-revelation and curiosity. Part of this process is the acknowledgment to one another of the ways we objectify ourselves and each other.

The Place of Objectification in the "I-You" Relationship

Objectification, as we have seen, is a normal process that is necessary in the early stages of psychological development. Unfortunately, people tend to become fixated in the objectifying process, and the further possibilities of intimacy and revealing become blocked.

Objectification is not bad; therefore, it is not necessary to stop it. To provide security, social conventions, and day-to-day order, objectification is a very efficient human tool. However, in the domain of intimate relationships, this objectification must be acknowledged as one's own, not as the "truth." In this way, people can share their judgments (objectifications) of each other through the process of the five A's (awareness, acknowledgement, acceptance, action and appreciation – see Chapter 1).

In dialogue, anything shared can enhance intimacy – this includes sharing fantasies, judgments, and objectifications. When people take responsibility for their objectifications, acknowledging that they are the ones doing the objectification, they establish personal boundaries. With this acknowledgement, the individual experiences more anxiety, but less objectification. Hence, the world of the Authentic Self opens up, yielding the possibility of genuine communication with the humanness of the other.

At the beginning, people who learn this often think that they should simply stop objectifying. But this would only be a denial, which would fixate them further; by trying to get rid of objectifications, people remain stuck with them. It is possible for individuals to learn to play with romance and other objectifications without making them their ultimate meaning. In the same manner, they can play with sexual charges, which are largely based upon objectification, without making them the end-all. Enter the theatre, enjoy the movie, and then go back into the street to continue with life!

There is a spiritual dimension to this. In surrendering to objectifications and revealing them without resistance, people can begin to let go of false ideas of themselves, and gradually become more in touch with their genuine nature. By acknowledging the objectifications of the "I-It," people can become curious about the personal world of the other, and move into the domain of "I-You," which permits authentic dialogue with another to occur.

Bridging and Healing

We discussed in Chapter 1 the experience of emptiness, disappointment and hollowness that so often comes with the betrayal of the Authentic Self. In bridging between self and others in the dialogue of intimate, "I-You" relationships, a person can learn to come to terms with this experience, which is a kind of internal rift, a separation of self from self. In healing a rift with someone else, people tend to heal the split within themselves too. It is tempting to believe that before you can love another, you must first learn how to love yourself; but it is more likely that you will learn to love yourself while you learn to love another. By bringing yourself forward and revealing yourself to another (an act of intimacy), you will discover how distant from others you have been, and how split off from yourself you have become. The awareness of those splits offers an opportunity to heal both gaps. When people reveal themselves to others, they become aware of the objectifications they have wreaked upon themselves; both self and other are recognized in such an intimate encounter.

> The unrelated human being lacks wholeness, for he can achieve wholeness only through the soul, and the soul cannot exist without its other side, which is always found in a "You." – C.G. Jung[8]

Part III

Relationships

For one human being to love another ... is a high inducement to the individual to ripen ... a great exacting claim upon us, something that chooses us out and calls us to vast things.

Rainer Maria Rilke[1]

9 **Intimacy**

An intimate relationship is a loving shared by two solitudes.[1]

In this chapter and the two that follow we give an overview of some important ideas about developing what we refer to as intimate relationships. As you read on you will see that we think of intimacy and sexuality as quite separate; an intimate relationship may or may not be sexual. Our focus here is on intimacy rather than sexuality. We deal with both intimacy and sexuality in much greater depth in *Joining: The Relationship Garden*. We hope that what we have to say here will stimulate you to investigate further and explore ways to enhance your own relationships.

Power or Intimacy in Relationships

In Chapters 2 and 3, we discussed in some detail the concept of a power-strength continuum, and linked this to a way of thinking about the Authentic, Ideal, and Actual aspects of a person. How people locate themselves along the power-strength continuum is a fundamental determinant of the kinds of relationships they will have.

Any relationship can be maintained from either a position of control (power) or a position of vulnerability (strength). In power-based relationships, people try to maintain security by controlling themselves and their partners. In the process, each plays a series of roles (e.g., good provider, competent mother, successful businessman). They submerge the Authentic Self beneath the myriad expectations of the security-based roles, and often experience a sense of dullness or deadness. The roles are effective but depersonalizing; hence, intimacy is restricted. Although seemingly more secure, relationships based on power are often rather brittle in nature, characterized by episodes of jealousy, anger, and anxiety when security is threatened.

The more that individuals are prepared to share all aspects of their inner world, including doubts, insecurities, pains, and fears, the more known to others they can be. Revealing is the cornerstone of an intimate relationship. Through vulnerability — being revealed to one another — increasing awareness of self and other becomes possible. The individuals in the relationship gain a sense of personal strength by revelation of all aspects of themselves, ideal, actual, and authentic. An intimate relationship is based on sharing rather than on need and security. The person-to-person exchange fosters increasing recognition of each person. Each remains compassionate and sensitive to the feelings of the other, without rushing in to try to take them away. Thus, each partner is met with respect in a caring and sensitive manner, and can flourish in the dialogue of individuating separatenesses. Embarking upon such an intimate relationship can arouse anxiety, possibly excitement, and often fear of losing control. The rewards can be individuation for both parties, discovery of more of one's authentic being, and a richer experience of life.

Intimacy is the condition of being known, one to another, through a close personal connection or experience. In interpersonal relationships, such "knowing" can occur in a number of ways. In usual circumstances, one person opens to the other in a conscious act of revelation, offering vulnerability. This vulnerability is usually accompanied by anxiety, related to the fear of being exposed and possibly hurt. On a social level, the issue for the individual is fear of rejection; on a psychological level, it is fear of loss of ego boundaries (experienced as loss of independence); on an ontological level, it is fear of death of the self.

The desire for intimacy and the motivation for offering oneself in face of such hazards arise from a yearning for the experience of connection with another person. Beneath social masks, people crave to overcome a deep sense of loneliness, the experience of being invisible (unseen, or not understood), and possibly a conviction of worthlessness.

In intimate relationships, people are willing to be vulnerable to each other, no matter how threatening that might be. With open, honest revelation, they develop deeper knowledge of themselves and each other. This is a person-to-person sharing, an "I-You" encounter in which both partners grow. Both persons are responsible for themselves, owning all the feelings that arise from their honest disclosures. There is no room for getting stuck in blame or victimhood. Partners in an intimate relationship value individual growth and respect for each other. Sensitivity to each other is a significant element in an intimate relationship.

Anything Shared Can Enhance Intimacy

Intimacy involves sharing; anything that is shared can serve to enhance intimacy. Sometimes, what people have to share is their desire to help one another, or their craving to be helped. It is important to be able to ask for help from each other when this desire occurs, acknowledging the extent of helplessness. Although leaning on one another could operate against intimacy if it became a fixed pattern, the acknowledgement of a desire to lean can also be a sharing that enhances intimacy. It is important to be able to be able to lean for a while, and not forever.

The question of power should be examined in all relationships. When one partner withholds from the other they are in fact, though often unconsciously, attempting to exercise control over the other. In an intimate relationship in which both persons are vulnerable, one does not control the other; both have their own individual strengths. For example, people often demand that their partners alter their behaviour to appease the hurt of jealousy. In an intimate relationship, sharing of hurt does not involve such control; instead, being responsible for their own feelings without blame enables both to experience and appreciate the pain. In an intimate sharing of hurts, it is possible that either one or both partners will not alter their behaviour.

In Chapter 11 we discuss anger as an example of how anything shared can enhance intimacy.

Principles for Creating and Maintaining an Intimate Relationship

- The welfare of the individual is more important than the welfare of the relationship. The relationship is not the goal; rather, it serves as a matrix for individual growth. The relationship is the garden; the individuals are the plants in that garden.

- Intimacy grows as partners reveal themselves to each other. In that revelation, they can discover more and more about themselves and each other. By moving out of roles, each becomes more individuated, making possible an increasingly person-to-person ("I-You") relationship. They become more visible and present. Rather than just acting in the world, they are being in the world.

- The tools of revelation are honesty and openness. Both individuals agree to reveal their processes, ideas, and feelings to the other as spontaneously and quickly as possible. When either decides to censor anything, this should be acknowledged. For example, keeping the details of the partner's birthday celebration a secret is worthwhile, and one could simply say "I'll tell you later, but for now, I'm censoring the answer to your question." Censoring restricts intimacy; but, since both parties are free to choose, they can accept some degree of censorship.

- Both persons are fully responsible for themselves. One person cannot be blamed for the other's feeling; there are no victims in an intimate relationship. Although neither is responsible for the feelings and experience of the other, each can be sensitive to the other's pain, anger, jealousy, and sadness. Although one party does not cause the feelings of the other, each can have caring and compassion for the other. Neither person should be controlled by the feelings of the other.

- When feelings are freely expressed and shared without blame, intimacy can develop. At first, it is often necessary for some feelings to be expressed with blame, in order to move the energy that accompanies those feelings. After the blame is expressed, both persons can then reassess the interaction, and both can take responsibility for their individual parts in the exchange.

- To maintain intimacy, feelings should not be used for control. A person's motives may be questioned by asking, "What is your intent in doing this?" It is important to check out suspicions, rather than assuming that they are facts. For example, it is preferable to responsibly ask, "I think I am being controlled by your tears (anger, laughter, etc.); is this what you intend?" rather than "Your tears (anger, laughter, etc.) make me feel guilty!"

- In a primary intimate relationship, partners agree that their relationship is the main focus of their intimacy. Intimacies shared with others are secondary to that primary relationship. In order to maintain the primary intimacy, anything shared with others would be acknowledged in the primary intimate relationship, so that there are no pockets of experience that are not included in the primary relationship.

- In establishing an intimate relationship, the many "immature" reactions and feelings that emerge (such as jealousy, blame, fear of abandonment, threatened loss of self-esteem, anger over unmet expectations) can be shared. In order to move toward intimacy – from controlling to sharing – both partners must then assume responsibility for their own responses and feelings.

- Any experience that is shared can enhance intimacy. For example, anger, which is often used in more dependent relationships as a form of control, can be shared without blame in order to enhance intimacy. When partners are vulnerable and revealed to each other, a mutual deep knowing becomes possible.

- Clearing – a process in which each partner acknowledges judgments, feelings, and intentions – is an important ingredient in the development and maintenance of intimacy. Defences and blockages will frequently emerge in one or both partners; clearing helps create an atmosphere in which each person can be revealed without blaming. A clearing is not complete until the person who has expressed asks for the experience of the other; without asking about the other, the one-sided expression is a "dumping," not a clearing.

- Objectification is counterproductive if not shared. The tendency to objectify is deeply rooted in the early development of each person. Examples of objectification include the tendency to view the other as a possession ("my husband"), as an object of desire ("my lover"), as a burden ("my obligation"), or as a purpose ("my reason to live"), instead of as the person that he or she is. Revealing the process of objectification is an excellent way to personalize the other, in order to move closer. At the same time, revealing objectification can be a source of excitement and challenge.

- Projection (ghosting, putting a hat on someone) interferes with clear communication. We are all prone to project, using our experiences from the past as the basis for interpretations in the present. The result is that we often tend to impute to our partner the motives and attitudes of people from our past, for example a parent. Realizing that these projections are not necessarily "accurate" and telling our partner about them is important to bring clarity and enable us to relate more with the person who is actually there.

- In an intimate relationship, partners will encourage and nurture any experience that is beneficial to the maturation and fuller expression of either person. Frequently, what stimulates growth in one is threatening to the other. When one person is threatened, this can be shared without controlling the behaviour of the other.

- As intimacy deepens, people become more visible to themselves and to each other; they develop a quality of presence. Intimacy is enhanced when each person agrees to be as present as possible in the company of the other, sharing all feelings and thoughts.

- Expectations of one another are not forbidden (contrary to some who decry all expectations). However, partners should reveal their expectations, and find agreement about them. Neither person is entitled to have expectations met. Often, power struggles arise when one partner has an expectation that the other person has never agreed to meet. We hold expectations to be of great value in an intimate relationship. When little importance is attached to another, expectations can be quite low; whenever another becomes more important, expectations of that person will be raised. Meeting mutually agreed upon expectations can be a challenge to the growth and development of both partners. However, it is important to remember that expectations should never be used for control; partners might voluntarily wish to live up to such expectations, but would have to freely do so, not through intimidation or threat. When one person decides not to live up to an expectation, the other might experience some hurt; in an intimate relationship, that hurt will be shared by both.

- Partners define themselves by setting boundaries and limitations in the relationship. Each can become present and revealed as desires and expectations are expressed.

- Sexual charge and intimacy are separate phenomena. Although they can be brought together in one relationship, there is a tendency for the sexual charge (which is rooted in objectification) to diminish as intimacy increases. This can be a creative challenge for couples who wish to keep sexual excitement alive and we devote a whole chapter to this important topic in *Joining: The Relationship Garden*.

- Guilt interrupts intimacy. When people feel guilty, they tend to withdraw from the contact boundary, indulging in self-recrimination. When guilt is acknowledged and shared, intimacy becomes possible again. Shame involves self-revelation, and tends to enhance intimacy. See Chapter 3 for more on the distinction we make between guilt and shame.

- Pride maintains distance; letting go of a prideful stance permits more intimacy.

- Having to be "right" results in an invulnerability that is destructive to intimacy. When both parties can have their own unique points of view without one or the other having to be right, then their intimacy can flourish.

- Time outs are useful. Whenever a conflict bogs down, either party can call "time out" – a period of time without processing – in order to find some breathing space, to gain a more balanced perspective. When either calls "time out," the request should be respected.

- Curiosity facilitates intimacy. When both parties are curious, they can work through the prideful, righteous stances that keep them at a distance.

- Blame kills intimacy. Whenever one person blames the other, no intimacy is possible. Partners can reveal their desires to react with blame, and choose instead to become responsible, examine their own participation in situations, and be curious about the other's experience.

We saw in Chapter 1 that it is possible to make an ideal of being authentic. So is it possible to make an ideal of intimacy. In both cases, the result is likely to be increasing self-hate. The key to get past this is to remember the 5 A's we outlined in Chapter 1, acknowledging to one another one's striving, one's successes and failures, one's doubts. In this way, people can develop increasing self-compassion and caring and empathy for one another.

Familiarity Is Not Intimacy

Unless there is openness, there is not intimacy. Familiarity occurs when people study and experience each other intently, without being open or revealed. Often family members learn much about each other by living together for a long time; unless they open with each other about deeper feelings, they will not be intimate. Athletes in competition can become very familiar with one another by studying and experiencing their opponents. In war, combatants often have a deep understanding of one another. Some interpersonal relationships maintain a level of excitement through challenge and control, developed through an appreciation of each other's strengths and weaknesses. In these situations, much is known about each other with little self-revelation. Although there is a quality of closeness in this familiarity, the relationship is not intimate; revelation and vulnerability are prerequisites of any intimate relationship. We quickly add that these occur on a continuum. In families, for example, there is often a mixture of familiarity and intimacy.

One-Sided Vulnerability

When only one person in a relationship offers revelations and vulnerability, the other person retains a position of power. This may occur in traditional medical and religious practices, for example, between social workers and their clients, or between parents and children. In these situations, to the degree that caretakers are not vulnerable or personal, they are hidden in conventions and expectations. This one-sidedness also occurs in many interpersonal relationships, where there is a high degree of dependency and caretaking.

In these situations, one person takes care of the other; in an intimate relationship, the people care about each other. In one-sided relationships, people must deal with issues of authority, dependence, obligation, possessiveness, jealousy, and privacy. More intimate relationships, on the other hand, foster self-development, growth, respect, acceptance, and responsibility.

Often in primary relationships, one person is more willing to be open and vulnerable than the other. This may vary over time and in different situations. We think there is strength in vulnerability, whether or not it is reciprocated. The more vulnerable person in such relationships can know that relationships go through stages (as we outline in *Joining: The Relationship Garden*) and that people open and close when they choose. They might also acknowledge their own desire to control their partner's behaviour ("I'm being vulnerable, so you should too!") There is always potential for learning! And ultimately people must choose what kind of relationships they want and what they are willing to do to create such relationships.

Loving Shared by Two Solitudes

The path of intimate relationship is not for everyone. Many people do not want this kind of relationship. The rewards of intimacy, however, include personal growth, the experiencing of authenticity and personal freedom, the sharing of aloneness, and a sense of fulfilment. The prerequisite is courage in two whole persons. To be intimate, both partners grow strong in their own separateness, sharing without depending. In the process, they contend with their idealizations about how things should be, and develop increasing self-compassion, and caring for their partners.

Loved

The path to healing is one which leads into discomfort
There is no easy way to open old wounds
  without allowing them to bleed
And pain is so often the price of awareness, wisdom and love

Warriors may choose to walk alone
  experiencing life's dramas with power and fortitude
  crying in silence, dying in isolation
They become the heroes — the glorified
  but rarely the loved

Love comes in sharing
  watching, feeling and allowing
  my pain to mix with yours
It is in these shared experiences I find my strength
  to face life's dramas with faith and confidence

For I am not alone
Your tears have become my strength,
  my courage to let go of my own
I treasure the tears we have shared
  just as I treasure our joy
It leads me down my path
  less afraid to bleed

Taking the steps to healing
  not dying in isolation
No hero
  worn and torn
... LOVED!!

— Susan Clarke

10 **The Communication Model**

In the previous chapter we described intimacy as a loving shared by two solitudes. The communication model we outline in this chapter is the principal method that we have used to develop such a relationship for ourselves. On one level, this model simply describes a process that goes on within each person. On another, it proposes that by revealing that process to another, and being curious about the other's experience, it is possible to build connection, clarity, and intimacy in a relationship. To use the model requires that people access and develop their strength as we have defined it in this book (Chapters 2 and 3).

We describe the following aspects to include in communication.

- Context
- Perception
- Interpretations and checking them out (bridging the gap)
- Feelings
- Intention
- Action

For the sake of clarity we describe these elements sequentially, though in reality they will each be foreground at various times for different people. The diagrams on the facing page are intended to show that communication is a repeating cycle of these overlapping elements and that *it takes two to communicate*. The key to turning a monologue into a true dialogue is checking out one's interpretations and developing curiosity about the other person. This creates a bridge between two people.

CONTEXT (BACKGROUND)

Each time you enter a new situation, you carry with you a context that is based upon your past experience (both recent and more distant). You do not enter new situations fresh; you colour them in terms of other experiences you have had. For example, if you have been having a bad day and feel irritable, when you meet a new person you will probably begin your interaction in an irritable frame of mind. On the other hand, if you have been feeling buoyant and happy and then enter a difficult situation, you are more likely to begin in a positive frame of mind. To give an example of a context from a more distant past, if as a child you had a frightening experience with a big dog, this may affect your experience of meeting the neighbour's Rottweiler for the first time!

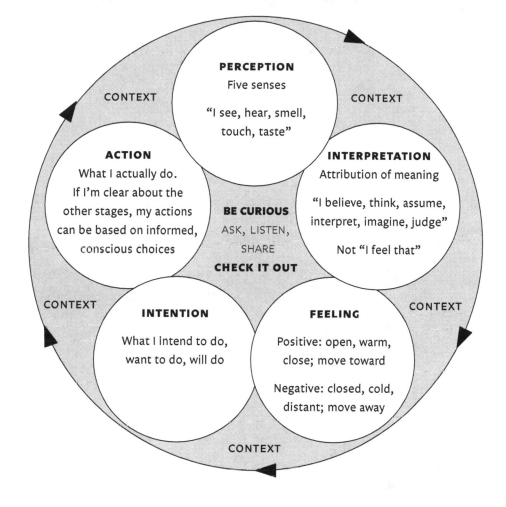

PERCEPTION
Five senses

"I see, hear, smell, touch, taste"

CONTEXT

CONTEXT

ACTION
What I actually do.
If I'm clear about the other stages, my actions can be based on informed, conscious choices

BE CURIOUS
ASK, LISTEN, SHARE

CHECK IT OUT

INTERPRETATION
Attribution of meaning

"I believe, think, assume, interpret, imagine, judge"

Not "I feel that"

CONTEXT

INTENTION
What I intend to do, want to do, will do

FEELING
Positive: open, warm, close; move toward

Negative: closed, cold, distant; move away

CONTEXT

CONTEXT

It takes two to communicate, so:

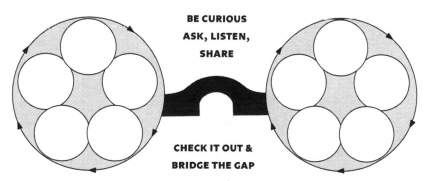

BE CURIOUS
ASK, LISTEN,
SHARE

CHECK IT OUT &
BRIDGE THE GAP

Think of agreeing or disagreeing with one another, rather than being right or wrong. Be curious about each other's realities. Also be clear with one another about your intentions as you communicate.

The context is the background or substrate against which immediate situations are viewed. Thus, one can benefit from a periodic checking with one's internal world to see what that context is. One should not take the context for granted, as it can shift and change. A moment of closing your eyes to investigate thoughts and feelings will give you an impression of the background you bring in. As you observe your thoughts and note your feelings, you will find what might be seen as trivial experiences – repetitive thoughts, or a vague mood that doesn't seem to have any origin. Note these – they will be colouring the situations you enter. Indeed, the context will even help select, out of the infinite variety of possible perceptions, those that you will notice.

PERCEPTION (THE FIVE SENSES)

As you open your eyes to observe another person, you will begin to absorb information about that person. In a matter of seconds you will take in hundreds, maybe thousands, of items of information through your senses – seeing, hearing, smelling, tasting, and touch. Mostly subconsciously, you quickly take in a vast array of data. What is interesting is that none of these pieces of information means anything in itself – the data are simply the result of stimulation of your nervous system. They are experienced by your brain as raw sensory information – shape, colour, texture, smells, and sounds.

Note that these are often subtle impressions – a fragrance, a sound, a movement on the face of the other. In order to make our world understandable, we go to work subconsciously on each of these pieces of information to make them mean something – that is, we perform the mental operation of interpreting. In the process, we also filter these perceptions to decide which we will bring more foreground in our consciousness; if we didn't do this, we would be overwhelmed by the sheer quantity of data. The perceptions are sensory; interpreting is the mental operation that provides the meaning.

INTERPRETATIONS (ATTRIBUTION OF MEANING)
... AND CHECKING THEM OUT (BRIDGING THE GAP)

As you observe your partner, you will have impressions of the way he or she is sitting; the colour of skin; the position of hands; the colour and type of clothing, jewelry, skin tone, hair style; and countless other features, including their words and tone of voice. From these impressions, you will assemble an overall picture, which you interpret. Now, it is important to realize that your interpretations are neither "right" nor "wrong" – they are best guesses at the meaning of what you are witnessing. These interpretations assist you in making intelligible the huge amount of information that you have received from your senses. They are simply your way of understanding the information you have.

One should always check with the other person, seeking agreement or disagreement relating to each interpretation. Again, it is not a question here of being right or wrong; I can only check to see if my version of you matches your version of yourself, or if my experience of an event matches yours. If you agree with me, I am not right, and if your opinion differs, this doesn't mean I am wrong; we simply agree or disagree. Our experiences are similar or different. When there is a difference in an interpretation, we can become curious about the different viewpoints we have, and learn more about ourselves and each other. This attitude of curiosity with no right or wrong permits an openness to ongoing learning; to become fixated on who is right or wrong brings learning to a halt.

Checking out interpretations, asking and listening with curiosity and an open heart and mind are the crucial steps that allow the transformation of monologue into dialogue. This is how people can "bridge the gap" between them.

Common phrases to express interpretations (and check them out) are:

- I interpret that you are a kind person. (Do you think of yourself that way?)

- I believe that you are being honest. (Are you?)

- I think that you are shy. (Is that your experience?)

- I assume that this is difficult for you. (Is that what is going on for you?)

- I imagine that you are uncomfortable. (Are you?)

- I judge that you are trying very hard to communicate. (Are you?)

- I speculate that you are thinking of something else. (Are you distracted?)

- I have an idea that you are feeling very anxious. (How are you feeling?)

Interpreting is a mental operation that involves thinking. A common mistake is to confuse interpretations with feelings. Thus the phrase "I feel that you are" usually does not introduce a feeling; instead, it is a misrepresentation of "I think that you are..." We think it is very helpful for people to include real feelings (which we discuss below) in their conversation; this can be made more difficult when people are unclear what are their feelings and what are their thoughts.

Many people are afraid to express their interpretations because the idea of judging someone else has taken on negative overtones. Yet judging (interpreting) is merely your way of making sense of information in order for you to more profoundly know another person. Judgment does not necessarily imply a rejection; indeed, pure judgment simply involves drawing distinctions in order to make sense of random data. It is from these interpretations that all your feelings come: how you interpret the data of your senses will determine whether you wish to move toward or away from another person.

FEELINGS

Based on the interpretations you make, you will develop your feelings. Feelings are experiences in the body involving changes in blood flow and energy shifts. There are basically two kinds of feelings, which we label positive (moving towards) and negative (moving away). We do not mean by this that one kind of feeling is good and the other bad. Rather, you might picture the image of a car battery where both poles are necessary if the battery is to work.

Positive feelings involve an opening up of the blood vessels in the body, and are associated with a sensation of warmth and well-being. When you sense this positive feeling, you will be drawn toward the person for whom you have the feeling. You might express a positive feeling in these ways: "I like you," "I am drawn to you," "I am attracted to you," "I feel comfortable with you," "I feel close to you," "I feel warm with you," or "I love you." The overall experience is one of feeling close and comfortable, with a desire to move toward the other person.

Negative feelings involve a contraction of the blood vessels in the body, with an accompanying feeling of tightness, discomfort, coolness and a desire to move back. You might express a negative feeling in any of these ways: "I am uncomfortable with you," "I dislike you," "I feel distant from you," "I am afraid of you," "I hate you," or "I feel like moving away from you." The overall experience is one of feeling distant, cool, wanting to move away. Children are quite willing to express such negative feelings, and let them go. As adults, we are often more reluctant to speak so directly; yet, such expression can facilitate communication.

Note that a negative feeling does not imply that the other person is bad or wrong; it simply reflects a judgment within the person who has the negative feeling, who for some reason experiences a desire to move away. For example, when you chose your outfit this morning, you were negative to all the other clothes in your closet; when you choose chocolate ice cream, you are negative to all the other flavours that you could have chosen. So, negative and positive feelings involve choice and valuing; they do not say anything about the worth of the other person, but rather speak of the valuing process within the person having the feelings.

Also, be aware that the feelings you have are based upon your context and interpretations. The same perceptions can be coloured differently given different contexts and interpretations, and it is possible to feel either positively or negatively about any perception. For example, the sight of a big man with a knife could be interpreted in various ways. If one were to interpret the man as a threatening killer, one would likely have a negative feeling and draw away; if instead one were to interpret him as a chef who is about to carve a roast of beef, one might draw close to get the first piece! The feelings are determined by the interpretations of the perceptions.

For this reason it is useful to tell your partner the feeling that accompanies your interpretations. For example, if you have the interpretation, "I think you are very smart," your feeling may be one of admiration, warmth and drawing close or it may be that you are intimidated and want to move away. Thus, we can revisit a few of the examples we gave a few pages back, this time including feelings:

- I interpret that you are a kind person. I feel relaxed and warm with you. Do you think of yourself as a kind person?
- I believe that you are being honest. I feel scared. What is going on for you?
- I think that you are shy. I feel awkward and rather distant. Are you shy, or is something else going on?

Note too, that in these examples, the speaker takes responsibility for his or her own feelings. When people say, as they very commonly do, "You make me feel relaxed/scared/awkward," their words suggest that the other person is responsible for their feelings. In effect, they are making themselves either dependent on the other person to feel good or, when they feel bad, the other person's victim. We recommend that people pay attention to their language not merely to be "correct," but to highlight for themselves the challenge of taking responsibility for their own feelings. To the extent that people learn to be responsible for their own feelings (and indeed their perceptions and thoughts) they can access their own autonomy and strength to also act responsibly in their daily lives.

INTENTION

Intention involves the conscious use of the will in translating feelings into action. For each perception/interpretation/feeling complex, it is possible to develop an intention about what you would like to do in response. You do not ever have to follow a feeling; human beings have free will, and can decide to act in opposition to their feelings. For example, you might feel attracted to someone, and decide not to pursue this attraction because of commitment to an established relationship. In a similar manner, you might be afraid of someone and decide to approach that person to talk about your fear, instead of withdrawing and following the feeling. You can always learn about yourself from a situation, whether you follow your feeling or not.

Also, you should be ready in a dialogue to ask of the other, "What is your intention in telling me this?" This question can shift an encounter to the level of the deeper meanings involved in the communication. For example, if someone's intention were to express anger in order to clear the air and become closer to you, you might be interested in staying to face the anger; on the other hand, if that person's intention was simply to try to intimidate or get control of you, you might not want to stay engaged. Clarifying your intentions can allow the communication to proceed to deeper levels.

ACTION

Action proceeds from decisions. Often this is an unconscious process; but, using the communication model, it can be brought increasingly into awareness. Once you can reflect on the process, you can make more conscious choices to take actions that are commensurate with your values and wishes. When you are aware of yourself and the other person or people, you are in a better position to make informed decisions about what to do.

The context for all your actions is determined by decisions you make about whether to be open or closed, to be curious or defended, to move towards others or away from them, to connect or disconnect. All of this informs your actions.

We are always making choices, whether we are aware or not. When we are not aware of the choice-making process – which involves our context, perceptions, interpretations and feelings – it can seem as if life just "happens" to us. When we realize that we are able to make conscious choices, our actions can be responsive to our experience of our selves and each other. We take more responsibility for our actions. With this comes extraordinary freedom, and often anxiety.

Once you become clear about your perceptions, interpretations, feelings, and intentions, and become curious about the experience of others too, your decisions to act will be less complicated, more easily understood by others, and more effectively executed. By working with this process, you can develop increasing amounts of self-responsibility, and your inner strength will grow. In this way you can develop considerable ability to respond to each situation in ways that you choose.

You are free to choose, and what actions you freely take shape your life. This opens up enormous possibilities for personal growth, expansion and transformation!

The Soup

As we have already noted, we have described these phenomena of communication sequentially; however, it is not necessary to proceed in the order we have described. One can start anywhere, and relate the other elements as they come up. For example, some people can readily relate their interpretations, and have to search to find their feelings; other people will easily know their feelings, and will not know the interpretations that are associated. The elements of the communication process are mixed together, just as different foods are mixed in a soup. Different elements become more foreground at different times. There is no right way or order to relate all this. Just begin, and describe to your partner the elements that you find. And don't forget that it takes two to communicate; check things out and be curious about one another's experience.

11 Anger: An Example of Sharing Feelings Responsibly

We have made the point before that anything shared can contribute to building intimacy between people. In this chapter, we look at one of the feelings that people often find hardest to share. We think that learning to share anger and "negative" feelings responsibly, safely and with boundaries is crucial to people's mental and physical health and to maintaining intimate relationships.

For many years until her death in 2007, our colleague Joann Peterson taught a program at The Haven called Anger, Boundaries and Safety; should you wish to look more deeply into this important topic, we highly recommend both the program (which is still offered) and Joann's book of the same name.[1]

Two key assumptions have underpinned our work with people around anger: first, that anger and violence are very different phenomena; and second, that people are responsible for their own feelings, as well as their thoughts and actions.

Anger and Violence Are Different

Many people have moral judgments against anger because they think it has negative effects upon others. These people, and society as a whole, confuse anger with violence. Anger itself is not dangerous or destructive; anger is a feeling of which people can find safe emotional expression while remaining respectful of the boundaries of others. What produces problems is the use of anger for control. When that happens, anger is expressed in ways that cross the boundaries of others; this we refer to as violence, which may be physical or verbal, direct or indirect, gross or subtle.

By this definition, violence can occur even when positive feelings are expressed in ways that violate another's personal boundaries, without the agreement of the recipient. Many parents, for example, "love" their children in violent ways, forcing them to do many things "for their good." For example, parents can do violence in the name of love by insisting that the children take music lessons when the youngsters vehemently do not want to do so. When people reveal that they are afraid of anger, it is often because in their earlier experiences anger was often expressed through violence (not only physical violence, but also sometimes mental or emotional violence).

Responsibility for Feelings

As we noted in our discussion of the communication model in Chapter 10, all feelings, including anger, are generated within a person and are based upon that person's interpretations of reality. Nobody can make me happy or angry; I become (I make myself) happy or angry over what I perceive and interpret others as doing. In this way, I alone am responsible (but not to blame) for all my feelings. When I fully understand this, I can step out of the victim role and take charge of my emotional life, developing a strength that furthers my personal growth. In that process, the power inherent in the victim role is abandoned in favour of effective communication.

The Genesis of Anger

It is our assumption that there is a primary underlying drive in human experience – the drive toward unity and joining, to return to the sense of oneness that ended at birth. This is counterbalanced by inevitable separations that occur throughout life.[2] Faced with such separations, as well as the basic, primordial fear of annihilation we discussed in Chapter 6, people experience deep anxiety and feelings of aloneness. This motivates them to establish meaningful relationships, in which they might re-experience that sense of union that is sometimes referred to as "love." When that is interrupted or unfulfilled, they experience frustration, fear, helplessness, or some variety of emotional pain, which motivates them to act. Infants often wish to control those upon whom they depend to meet their basic physical and emotional needs; infantile behaviours are often carried on into adulthood. For children, crying and the myriad other forms of complaint are common ways of attempting to bring caretakers under control. If these do not readily work, they experience frustration, more fear and helplessness, and then anger! Anger can be seen then as a means of overcoming the helplessness that can arise as a result of prolonged frustration.

Anger Is Not a Primary Feeling

In this account of its genesis, anger is a secondary rather than a primary feeling; usually, beneath it there is hurt or a sense of helplessness. This hurt commonly arises when expectations are not met; the person with the expectations may experience disappointment, and possibly much emotional pain. Instead of continuing to experience that pain, which would contribute to a feeling of helplessness, the person might unconsciously convert the pain into anger. Anger provides an energy that fills the individual with a sense of power, overcoming the desperation of helplessness. This can be extremely useful if a person learns to use it responsibly. However, people often use their anger to bully or manipulate others into living up to their expectations; that is, they use it violently. This is often effective, because people are so ready to accept blame for other people's hurts. Also, many individuals are intimidated into compliance because they too have had childhood experiences in which anger was accompanied by violence.

Sharing Anger

If people can share their anger in an open and responsible fashion, without blame or control, energy that might otherwise be stuck is mobilized. In the process people stand revealed and vulnerable, and this could be an opening for intimacy. In relationships, such sharing involves an engagement between the persons, an intimate contact with an accompanying sense of aliveness and excitement. However, to be effective, this requires the establishment of some fundamental guidelines:

- There must be an agreement to absolutely no violence; that is, everybody's boundaries must be respected. For example, nobody will be hit or hurt in any physical way. Other boundaries will be established, some of which are discussed below. To cross any of these would constitute violence.

- There must be no physical damage to material things, other than those designated and agreed by all parties concerned (for example, pillows that can be punched or sheets that can be torn).

- Either person can call a stop to the proceedings at any time, especially out of fear or concern for either party.

- The boundaries of location and time (for example, for fifteen minutes, in the living room) must be agreed upon before starting. Extensions can be negotiated at the end of that time.

- The inclusion/exclusion of third parties (for example, the children or other members of the household) must be agreed upon beforehand.

- The use of blame, foul language, put-downs, and so on can be allowed if the parties agree, with the proviso that at the end these will be owned in a responsible way. These can be negotiated in specific cases, should they deviate from a person's baseline of acceptable behaviour.

The above agreements remove the possibility of using anger to control one another through violence; instead the anger can be shared, to deepen the intimacy in the relationship. It is important that at the end of such sharing, both partners spend time in clarifying the issues that lie beneath the generation of anger, being careful to use clear responsible communication and avoiding blame and righteousness (and acknowledging them if they do arise). Each person must accept the responsibility for his or her own feelings in order for this to be effective.

Anger, Assertion and Violence

Some people confuse assertion with anger and violence. When people stand firmly behind their convictions about themselves, without condemning others' viewpoints, they stand forth from the crowd; this is not to be confused with self-righteousness, where a person with rigid moral values sees others as being wrong. When people are assertive, they neither apologize nor succumb to soliciting the approval of others. Because such people tend to stand forth rather than blend in, others might become anxious, believing they are being criticized, when actually assertive people are simply expressing their own position. It is important to know the difference, and exceedingly useful to check out the intention of the other. Self-assertive persons confirm their own being by expressing their opinions while remaining respectful of the views of others.

Indirect Anger

If anger is not expressed directly, it usually comes out in a great variety of indirect ways. A hostile person can be smiling and friendly, while manipulating events to try to hurt others. Negative gossip can be an expression of repressed anger; so too can the process of undermining another's authority or credibility. Sometimes anger is masked by over-niceness or over-attentiveness; these are often attempts to compensate for negative feelings. When people do not express anger directly, it can wear on them in the form of psychosomatic symptoms such as headaches, peptic ulcers, colitis, teeth grinding, hypertension, and sleep disturbances (including nightmares). When people direct their repressed anger against themselves, they can move into depression, addictions, and a wide variety of other self-destructive behaviours.

Transforming Anger

Instead of repressing and masking anger, people can learn to transform it, by expressing it in socially acceptable, self-enhancing and relational ways.

Participation in aggressive sports and competitive games are two examples of such a strategy; these only become destructive when the pleasure in the sport is converted into an obsessive need for dominance. Anger can also be used to ignite the aggressive drive of the crusader and political critic, who serve to keep society informed about its shortcomings. Anger can provide the energy so that people can rise out of conditions of poverty and helplessness through education or advancement in employment.

In all of these examples, the constructive element of such transformations is lost when people become insensitive to the rights and boundaries of others; when anger is expressed insensitively (as in revenge), it becomes destructive and opposes growth. When people mix anger up with blame, treating themselves as victims, they then can become involved in a malignant pattern of seeking revenge. Their anger then becomes obsessive and hateful, breaking up relationships and tending to leave the person isolated and more insecure. Rather than increasing the person's vitality in life (as occurs when anger is shared), such expression of anger wears out people's bodies and feelings, rendering them less effective in life.

Anger can serve a useful purpose by providing energy, so that people can mobilize themselves into action. Invigorated, they can lift themselves out of a state of helplessness and sometimes depression, and move toward resolution of a problem. Anger is an integral part of life experience; don't exclude it, either from yourself or others you love. Especially in intimate relationships it can be a source of great energy and connection.

Just as it can be useful to responsibly express anger with a partner, so sharing any feeling with another can enhance closeness and mutual understanding. In *Joining: The Relationship Garden* we explore ways of sharing a range of feelings, including jealousy, resentment, guilt, or fear, as well as pleasure and loving.

Part IV

Health and Healing

I am not a mechanism, an assembly of various sections.
And it is not because the mechanism is working wrongly,
    that I am ill.
I am ill because of wounds to the soul,
    to the deep emotional self
and the wounds to the soul take a long, long time,
    only time can help
and patience, and a certain difficult repentance
long, difficult repentance, realisation of life's mistake and
    the freeing oneself
from the endless repetition of the mistake
which mankind at large has chosen to sanctify.

D.H. Lawrence[1]

12 Learning in Illness and Health

Disease is nothing but life under altered conditions. – Rudolf Virchow[1]

Victims of Illness

From earliest times, people have attempted to stay well by avoiding physical dangers and hostile environments. Since their survival may have depended on it, this was often a wise thing to do. At the same time, feeling threatened and uncertain, humans developed superstitious beliefs in powerful spirits and gods that could do harm to individuals, sometimes just for sport. In recent centuries, scientific investigations have discovered a great number of causative agents (bacterial, viral, and chemical) that can negatively affect a person's well-being. Superstitious beliefs have developed around these entities too; in some ways, they have become our modern spooks and goblins. The line between sensible precaution and paranoia is often unclear.

People frequently cast themselves in a paranoid, adversarial role in relationship to the environment, with sometimes drastic consequences. For example, we may think that unless we take every measure to shield ourselves from the possibility of a viral attack, we will likely succumb to a cold. In this way we see ourselves as potential victims of invading forces that lack respect for our integrity and well-being. Excessive worry about these forces may lead us to avoid all sources of possible contamination, including other people, or set off a campaign to clean up the environment way beyond any reasonable standard. This paranoid attitude seems more and more common; with this view, people need to be vigilant in order to avoid ill health. They fortify their defences to protect them from these ever-present noxious invaders; in so doing, they also produce an increasing separation between themselves and their surroundings.

An Alternative: Responsibility and the Meanings of Disease

Many of these "enemies" are omnipresent, living in harmony nearby, perhaps even comfortably ensconced somewhere within our bodies. A simple example is the cold virus, which probably lives in most of our throats much of the time. Why then do we come down with a cold only at certain times? A common belief is that the virus has been waiting for the opportunity to "invade" our bodies, perhaps when we get overly tired or when we eat the wrong things. Another possibility is that sometimes a cold can be useful, that the helplessness it produces might serve us. Perhaps having a cold provides a rationalization for a much-needed rest which we otherwise would feel too guilty to take.

Certainly, as children we learn that helplessness can provide us with many secondary benefits – we may get attention, or be excused from chores, school, or work, and perhaps we even receive special foods. Is it possible that when we grow older, we are not above reaping the benefits of a cold?

If we acknowledge that this is so, then we can take responsibility for our own illness rather than see ourselves as its victim. It might also be possible to acknowledge one's need for a rest and take one, without resorting to a cold as a means to getting it!

The idea that we are responsible for our own illness patterns might help explain some apparently odd behaviour – why the obese continue to overeat or alcoholics continue to drink even though their actions are ruining their lives, or people with heart disease or emphysema continue to smoke. Although these people might like to believe that they are helpless victims of their addictions, it seems likely that they benefit in some way from their symptoms. Perhaps the obese person is attempting to pad the body as a means of avoiding intimacy; perhaps the alcoholic is afraid to face the possibility of failure, and drinks so that nobody will expect much; perhaps the smoker is keeping feelings under control because to express real emotions (such as anger or passion) might drive others away. Whatever the requirement, the body cooperates with symptoms of an illness process that serves the person's particular needs. Thus, whenever a person has symptoms, or a diagnosed illness, there is often an underlying meaning to be discovered. The body will speak what the mouth cannot, or will not!

Using Symptoms for Location

As we discussed in Chapter 7, one of our human tasks is to locate ourselves, and make a world for ourselves. In the midst of profound uncertainty and anxiety, humans struggle to find some dependable security. Remarkably, many people find predictability in suffering. Although they experience discomfort in illness processes, they also come to know these very well, and often are reluctant to give up their symptoms for fear of the emptiness that rises when they depart from what they know. Suffering is not pleasant, but it can be predictable and familiar. Thus, illnesses and various symptoms and different ways of suffering can provide a way for individuals to locate themselves.

Qi Energy and the Concept of Fixation

The ancient Chinese conceived of life force energy, which they called *qi* energy (pronounced "chee").[2] Their hypothesis was that this life force energy comes into the being at the time of conception, exists in the individual throughout his or her lifetime, and departs at death. During the person's life, the *qi* energy continually flows through meridian pathways; the pattern created by this flow constitutes the energy body matrix or energy body, which is the essential pattern of that being. This energy body is radiant, and manifests on various dimensions of a person – spiritual, emotional, physical, intellectual and even beyond the individual to influence the surrounding environment. In the view of the ancients, if the energy flow in the matrix is balanced and harmonious, the organism functions freely, without illness. Fixations in the energy body interfere with the harmony and balance of the flow of *qi*; this is manifest on the various dimensions of the person as symptoms of disturbance or disease. Everyone has some degree of fixation; these are the holding patterns that underlie the particular personality characteristics. When these fixations become severe, or persist for a long time, they can manifest as diseases. In terms of energy, we don't stop at our skin. We are in dynamic interaction with the *qi* patterns of other people, and the natural world. Just as individuals can become ill, the environment can be ill too. An example of this is the excess carbon dioxide in the atmosphere as a result of human activity.

Since these fixations are a product of people's life style and attitudes, each individual is responsible (but not to blame) for illness. The fixations may be generated and maintained by subconscious processes; nevertheless, even though these processes are out of awareness, at some level the individual is the one that maintains the patterns that manifest as diseases.

This is in accord with the existential viewpoint that people can choose how to deal with their own life situation. In this way, they are responsible for their contribution to health or illness through the lifestyle choices they make. Wherever illness is present – emotional, physical, spiritual, intellectual, or environmental – people are responsible for the creation and maintenance of the patterns that the illness reflects. Once again, this responsibility is not blame; it merely acknowledges the individual's participation. By accepting responsibility for sickness and health, one can move through and beyond illness patterns, into states of well-being and openness. In the process, one can learn about motives and fixations, and discover more of the hidden aspects of one's life.

Central to Chinese energy theory is the notion that the various dimensions of being are actually a unity. Complementary medical approaches speak of "mind/body" unity. The full descriptive term should be "body/mind/emotions/spirit/environment" unity. The apparent separateness of mind, body, spirit, emotions and environment is an expression of our unique human viewpoint, a byproduct of our nervous system and biology; yet, at a fundamental level, our various "parts" are integrally related to each other, they are each other. An illness on one level will show on the other levels. For example, from this perspective, there is no such thing as a physical illness separate from mental distress. Spiritual ailments are reflected in the mental state, in the body, and indeed in the environment. It is common for an illness state to be primarily on one of these dimensions; nevertheless, the process will also occur throughout the other dimensions, since they are a unity. It will be useful to bear this in mind as we discuss the various forms of fixation below.

Emotional Fixation

By withholding the expression of emotions, a person produces obstructions in the energy body matrix, which contribute towards disruptive patterns in the *qi* energy. These constricted patterns can manifest on the other dimensions of being as illness (physical disease, mental or emotional disorder, spiritual distress, or disturbances in the environment such as water pollution, unclean air, and so on). The mechanisms to inhibit emotional expression include withdrawal, repression, and denial. Emotions are held back through very limited breathing; when people learn to breathe more deeply, filling their lungs, they can find more ready expression of their emotions, and become more in touch with themselves. By becoming aware of the nature of these mechanisms, one can learn to express emotions instead of repressing them. The more the individual can let emotions flow, the more the life energy can run freely and the more that healing and awareness can develop. Often one encounters a great deal of fear overlaying the blocked emotions. By refusing to flee from the fear, people can allow the emotions to emerge; instead of contracting, they can open to more learning, and growth can occur.

Physical Fixation

Illness is also created and sustained on the physical level. Lack of exercise engenders sluggishness and disease. Certain exercises done in an ambitious, goal-oriented way tend to tighten the physical being into a particular pattern, producing restriction and lack of flow. These physical limitations correspond to a rigidly patterned energy body matrix. Goal-oriented athletic pursuits often maintain the rigidity; note that it is the goal-orientation that engenders the limitation, not the exercise itself. Expressive exercises, such as free-form *tai ji* and creative dance, tend to encourage fluid energy flow. Any exercise done creatively for self-expression can help to open up the person; any activity that is goal directed will invite contraction. And yet if certain people are goal-oriented types, they are unwise to simply deny their tendency; instead, they can learn to become more fluid, even in the midst of striving.

The maintenance of the open healthy state is also determined by what one ingests. A well-balanced diet engenders healthy functioning and growth, whereas an inadequate diet fails to provide the necessary nourishment. The abuse of alcohol, nicotine, and other drugs can also sustain blocks, limiting the natural self-expression.

Spiritual Fixation

Illness can manifest at the spiritual level; as well, fixations on the spiritual dimension can create illness. Victor Frankl said that "Man's search for meaning is a primary force in his life."[3] In creativity, people express meaning beyond their self-limitations. Frankl quotes Nietzsche: "He who has a why to live for can bear almost any how."[4] When this sense of meaning is lost, illness patterns may substitute for it; frequently, the illness becomes the meaning. To find personal meaning in life and to channel energy into creative activity aids the spiritual rebirth that generates health, well-being, and growth.

Overly disciplined spiritual activity can also result in blocks to free expression. Ambitious involvement in yoga, meditation, special diets, and other similar pursuits can limit the individual rather than expand awareness.[5] Spiritual ambition, making an ideal of certain spiritual states, is frequently the motivation for excessive discipline. In this ambition and the compulsive behaviour that results, a tightening occurs in the energy matrix, expressed as a contraction in the person. In a paradoxical way, the ambition to become spiritually expanded results in a contracted state. The first step in reversing this contraction is often through the awareness that excessive spiritual discipline can induce it; this awareness may facilitate greater expansion and freer self-expression.

Intellectual Fixation

Intellectual openness and fluidity sustain health and growth. Fixated intellectual patterns restrict the being; illness can result from such limitation. The intellect performs the symbolization of life experiences; one of its main functions is communication. Investment in specific concepts to the exclusion of others constitutes a rigidification into a judgmental attitude. We believe such an attitude is often reflected in the contraction in the energy state that underlies many illnesses. Acknowledging rigidity and working toward more intellectual flow and grace promotes healing and growth. With the assumption that one's attitude contributes to the creation and maintenance of illness, one can use symptoms as biofeedback alerting one to the possibility of attitudinal rigidity. By this process of awareness, we believe one can deeply influence the condition of the energy state.

Environmental Fixation

Fixation on any of the levels we have mentioned can manifest in the larger environment around us, including the lives of other people as well as the natural environment. Likewise, fixation on an environmental level can have profound effects on our wellbeing on every other level. Disruption in this complex interrelationship has perhaps never been so urgently apparent as it is today. While the topic is beyond the range of this book, we note here that fixated right/wrong struggles feature highly in many people's approach to climate concerns. Commonly, entrenched positions preclude a serious investigation of how to create more balance and harmony between humans and their environment.

Illness and Health in Relationships

People manifest their fixations in relationships, often defending themselves from each other because of fear or insecurity. In this holding back, they tighten in their energy, and this can ultimately manifest as illness.

When individuals have had a history of enduring violence or boundary violation, they are often reluctant to come close to others. They believe their hesitancy keeps them safe (as at one time it probably did). They develop patterns of withdrawal or defensiveness in order to protect themselves from violation. In this walled approach, they tighten in themselves, and set the stage for illness to take root.

We sometimes give a talk humorously entitled "Relationships Make Me Sick." Our main point is that illnesses arise from the fixated stances acquired in early relationships. These attitudes of tightness persist in later relationships; they give rise to distress on the various levels of being, and can ultimately manifest as full-blown illness states. The holding back in the relationship has produced the illness. We go on to say that an intimate relationship can be a garden where people can discover themselves, their loving, their meaning and their health and vitality; but this takes the courage to face difficult issues.

So, relationships are where people become stuck. Yet in relationships, people can also become free. When they are willing to engage in an ongoing relationship of intimacy and revelation, they can face the fear of coming close to someone else, and can thus open their capacity for engagement with their partners, with themselves, and with life. The relationship then becomes a place of healing.

Learning to Dialogue for Health

Our work together over more than four decades has focused on the relationships area. We are more and more convinced that illnesses are most often an expression of some separation. Healing occurs when the apparent separation is rejoined. Many human ailments arise in the domain of flawed relationships, with objectification and isolation being key factors in maintaining distance. People can heal from this by becoming vulnerable with each other, opening and revealing their authentic nature, becoming inclusive of the each other's world. Through dialogue, people can come to appreciate, know and love each other and themselves. To us, all healing occurs in dialogue. We discuss in more depth the healing aspects of dialogue in *The Illuminated Heart*.

People frequently come to programs at The Haven looking for help. They often approach the leaders in the traditional framework of seeking healing from a professional. If the leaders were to succumb to this invitation, people could remain tied to them, and fail to make use of the group process. In the group activities, people are invited to reveal their inner thoughts and feelings, becoming vulnerable with each other. As they do this over the days of a program, they establish deeper, more intimate relationships with other members of the group, and come to feel more at home with themselves. They practice open communication, and acquire skills that they can use to open with others when they choose; the group is like a learning laboratory where they develop skills of intimacy. Having learned and practised these skills, people can take these abilities into their significant life relationships (with family, spouses, lovers, and business associates), in order to develop and sustain ongoing intimacy. In this atmosphere, they learn to open themselves, to release the blockages in interpersonal energies. With this unblocking comes release of life flow; in this way, people are healed in the intimate relationships they develop.

In the healthy open state, people can grow and mature, to reach the full depth and expanse of self-expression and individuation. This does not mean it is possible to avoid all illness; rather, it means embracing whatever illnesses we have, and learning from them. Indeed, even the most serious illnesses can be an opportunity for discovery, as the poet Robert Duncan so poignantly writes:

> *Medicine can cure the body. But soul, poetry, is capable of living in, longing for, choosing illness. Only the most fanatic researcher upon cancer could share with the poet the concept that cancer is a flower, an adventure, an intrigue with life.*[6]

When partners share their feelings and experience with each other during an illness process, they can go deeper in their intimacy, sometimes in unexpected ways. Ernie McNally, a long-time core faculty member of The Haven, lives what he teaches. At the time of writing, he is undergoing treatment for a life-threatening brain tumour. He has chosen to affirm his relationships with his wife Cathy and his friends and family, and share his challenges and insights with them. He lives each day with richness and vitality, affirming life and relationship. He writes:

> *I believe in relationship. I strongly believe the reason that my health is beyond what any medical person has expected, given my diagnosis, is because of the strength that is alive in me through relationship, through contact with you, with caring, loving, honesty, touch. I am consciously aware of a different depth and breadth in my life, and feeling beyond what I have opened to in my life, because of relationship. I am healthier in every way because I love, and am loved, because I give and receive. I live in what a dear friend calls "leaving nothing unsaid." And through my belief, I am living well, with relationships that offer my body, spirit, mind ... and even my tumour ... health and healing.*[7]

In the following chapters, we discuss a number of conditions – allergies and phobias, multiple sclerosis, and depression – with which we have had considerable experience in our work with people. The principles we outline, however, are much more widely applicable and may be useful in many other disease processes.

13 Allergies and Phobias: A Matter of Self-Definition

Two Stories

To a casual observer Jane's life is highly successful. She is attractive, well educated, and has a good, well-paying job. But her outward appearance of success masks an inner turmoil that runs deep and disrupts the entire fabric of her life. Jane has been going from doctor to doctor for the past several years, trying to find someone who can explain the extreme, yet vague, symptoms that she experiences. And although many professionals have provided treatments, suggestions, and attention, she still suffers from myriad complaints with little relief. She is puzzled, frustrated, and frightened by what seems to be happening to her. Her inner life is a private hell. Whereas she used to have extraordinary vitality, she has been finding increasing difficulty getting through her work days. She sleeps a fitful 13-hour night; she feels tired all the time and does not have enough energy for her other interests or for keeping up socially. Her friends are beginning to stop calling; more and more, she is by herself at home in bed. Her life dreams are fading as she struggles to get through just one more day. She has been told that her headaches, listlessness, and nasal symptoms add up to an allergy syndrome. She feels a little better on a special diet that has been prescribed; yet, she is beginning to fear that she is never going to get well or regain her previous happy, carefree life.

Audrey, who has been experiencing similar fatigue symptoms in a city far away from Jane, seems to be in a different situation. Because of her intense fears of leaving her home, she has been told that she is "agoraphobic." She scarcely ever leaves her apartment; family and friends must come to visit her. Although she conducts her successful business from her home, she is coming to recognize that her life is closing in on her; yet, the thought of going out for an evening is so frightening to her that she simply refuses to date. The extreme anxiety she has been feeling for the past several years has been significantly reduced by her limiting her activities and by the large doses of tranquilizers and antidepressants that she takes daily; yet, with her diminished anxiety, she feels dulled. This attractive young woman is becoming more and more socially paralysed as her condition takes deeper hold.

Boundary Issues: The Common Thread of Self-Definition

There are many people living similarly restricted lives. On the surface, they may appear to be fine; but inside, they experience a desperate dread that something is not right. A significant number of young people are suffering from apparently different syndromes that have remarkably common underlying themes. Sometimes the diagnosis is "phobia"; at other times the label is "allergy," or even "total allergy syndrome." In these different conditions, there are unmistakable common threads that run through the separate stories. What accounts for the similarities in such an array of troubles?

Over the years, we have known a number of people who had been diagnosed in these ways. As we worked with them, we came to recognize that most of these people were dealing with issues of boundary distinction. Their symptoms were manifestations of the fact that, in some fundamental ways, they had not learned to define themselves.

A Medical Perspective: The Physiology of Boundaries

The immune system is a biological complex that functions to protect the integrity of the physical organism; with its various antibodies and neuro-chemical mechanisms, it is like an army that defends against outside invasion. The immune system maintains the boundary of the physical being, distinguishing and keeping out what is "not me" and holding in place what is "me." When a person's immune system malfunctions, disease states ensue. Allergy involves a hyper-reactivity to certain outside conditions (e.g., hay fever, drug hypersensitivity, food allergies); the defence is excessive. When the immune system is underactive, as in extremely debilitated states or in illnesses such as HIV/AIDS, the person is physically vulnerable to assault from what might ordinarily be harmless circumstances. For example, a person with a lowered immune defence system is more susceptible to infections and is less able to fight them effectively.

A Psychological Perspective: Separation and Individuation

In object relations theory, the infant "hatches" from the mother-infant "symbiotic dual unity" during the process of ego development. The developmental project for children is to become a separate human being by acquiring a sense of themselves that is distinct from the mother (and by extension, distinct from the environment). Research now suggests that there is early differentiation even in utero and that very young infants are more aware of their environment, including the desires and motives of others, than previously suspected. Certainly, this project is well established by two years of age, when the child is first learning to move away from parents and caregivers while still craving the protective milieu of love and acceptance from the big person. Thus, youngsters are in a process of separation (learning to be psychologically and physically separate from the mother) and individuation (developing a unique sense of themselves in an individual life experience).

For many children, this process is not smooth; the child either hastily and prematurely splits from the parent instead of developing an organic separation, or does not separate, remaining symbiotically and dependently bound to the psyche of the parent. In a sense, the child either develops brittle and artificial boundary distinctions (walls) or remains to some extent undifferentiated from the parent. The former is analogous to hyperactivity of the immune system; the latter is analogous to inadequate immunity to the outside world. In later relationships, these early defensive patterns of splitting without relating, or fusing without distinction, are likely to be reproduced. These processes probably are psychological correlates of much of what are dubbed "allergies" and "phobias."

A Chinese Medicine Perspective: The Earth Element

In the framework of the five stages of change in classical Chinese medicine, the issues of the earth phase are those of incarnation. In other words, the human body is the medium through which the other dimensions of being are expressed and made manifest. The definition of the individual takes shape and form through the mediation of the earth energies. The earth issues are involved with relationships, the physical being, separation/union, the mother/child interaction, and nurturing. Individuals with difficulties in the earth aspects of the energy body matrix will exhibit symptoms in the body, in relationships, and in self-definition. Thus, from a Chinese medical viewpoint, people with allergies and phobias have some disturbance in the earth phase of their energy body.

The Story Underlying Allergies and Phobias

As we worked with people troubled by allergies and phobias, we began to see other, related, themes that characterized their individual experiences. The boundary issues we saw as central to the process were expressed in some quite striking ways.

The people we met were often highly intelligent and creative. Hence, they were somewhat unwilling to follow a standard life path. At the same time, however, they were generally very frightened of the passions that surged through them; they commonly feared their erotic impulses, were anxious about their high level of energy, and afraid of the unusual thoughts that passed through their minds. These creative individuals were unwilling to live a commonplace existence; yet, without sufficiently developed boundaries to help them determine where they belonged and what they wished to do in the world, they were cast into an existential maelstrom of anxiety and uncertainty. They resisted succumbing to the safety of the standard cultural patterns (a job, getting married, raising children); yet they were reluctant to risk a full-fledged creative life. They were therefore caught in the hinterland between the commonplace and the unique. They walled themselves off from the regular world with an illness process; in a sense, they became "allergic" to the commonplace, or developed "phobias" that protected them from conventionality.

Deep down, these people experienced despair, because they were not fully engaging with their lives; this despair was commonly supplanted by symptom complexes. The bulk of their creative energy was dedicated to producing an illness metaphor in which they could justifiably live. Instead of devoting themselves to artful living, they became increasingly enslaved by the illness system that they had created and maintained. In a way, their illness provided social justification for their unusualness, without the risks of full-blown creativity. The uncertainty of the creative impulse was reduced to the predictability of an illness condition ("I couldn't possibly go there" or "I can't handle that.")

These people were generally under 40, intelligent and attractive beyond the usual. All of them experienced varying degrees of anxiety, fatigue, lessened energy, disturbance of sleep patterns (for example, sleeping up to 13 or 14 hours per day without being refreshed), bodily tensions, and symptoms related to eyes, ears, nose, and throat. They were increasingly socially isolated. Although this was often rationalized ("I'm allergic, so I can't go there... eat that... do this"; "I simply have to get 12 hours of sleep"; "I'm afraid to go out at night – it's a phobia"), there was frequently an underlying fear of intimacy. Their relationships tended to be dependent; they would not risk the uncertainty that would accompany the vulnerable exposure of themselves in intimacy and interdependency.

In summary, these people were afraid to face the passion and the creativity that coursed through them. They were afraid of vulnerability and had a high need for control. They experienced themselves as victims of life, and adopted a stance in which "life does it to me." They often believed that those who follow cultural convention are enslaved and dead. However, they themselves became trapped in their victim stance, which kept them imprisoned in the cage of their illnesses.

The View from Inside

The following are accounts from people we have worked with over the years.

I created total allergy syndrome. I experience a great fear in becoming vulnerable and have throughout my life often denied intimacy because of that fear.

I also experience life very intensely: my emotional range consisted of jagged peaks of joy, even ecstasy, and very deep sadness and pain. The instability that I experienced from this caused much despair in my life, and I sought ways of becoming stable.

I see total allergy syndrome as an extension of this disconnectedness from my essential self and as a reaction to the denial of my natural life.

I am terrified of being who I am. I see myself as a little boy overawed by life and fearful of the pain and sadness that I find in life.

Another young person relates:

My illness is the result of a lack of self-expression.

Another:

Basically, I am finding that there is something emotional or psychological (that is, ingrained attitudes, behaviours, and suppressed feelings, needs, and desires) behind every physical allergic reaction. Awareness of the underlying factors improves the symptoms and allows me to take charge and control them much of the time.

And another:

The challenges in my life were masked in attacking the same mundane exercises day in and day out year after year after year.

I created the fears and these fears help me to survive situations I otherwise would not look at.

I haven't the means to know what would constitute "value" in my life... I now know that I have to find my own definition of worth and make a strong and fully conscious decision to live it.

This place of desolation is a large part of my pattern; it comes up over and over again starting very early in my childhood memories.

What I've realized here at The Haven is that my stubborn resistance to my own mortality only serves to further fuel my feelings of fear and anxiety. I also feel that I isolate myself from others at these times and become very lonely.

The Way Out of the Trap

We have worked with numerous people over the past 40 years who have made significant improvement in these conditions. They have struggled to take more responsibility for themselves and their life circumstances (including their symptoms). The statements above bear witness to this struggle. As they came to see that anxiety is just the life energy coursing through them, these people learned to embrace increasing amounts of anxiety. As their tolerance for anxiety increased, they were able to face one of their largest fears: that of being close to another human being. As they took increasing responsibility for their process, they began to understand the secret codes of the illness metaphor; they came to see the symptoms as messages from their inner being, calling for reunion with themselves. In a way, the illness, which previously was an enemy, became a friend. At bottom, they were afraid of nonexistence. They were afraid to stand on their own and face another person. They were either isolated, or refrained from intimate contact by maintaining dependent relationships.

The following words speak for themselves:

I've learned that anxiety can be energy running through me.

I no longer fit into a mould of what I think I should be. I just am, marching to a different beat.

Everything I hold or lock in makes me sick. I need and want to be around people I can let go with.

I believe that I am well, whole, integrating... that I have learned and know all I need to be well and express myself in the world. What I need and want to do now is develop the self-love and confidence to trust it and do it.

I also realize that I must surrender myself to the pain, to the sadness, in order to experience the joy and intimacy that life will provide.

I seek now the courage within myself to surrender and to live.

Acceptance of the Illness Process

The courage that we have witnessed in people facing these difficult issues has been inspirational. As they have taken responsibility for their illness process, they have opened to their own life and creativity again. Instead of fighting illness, they learned to acknowledge it, accept it, and work with it. One person put it this way:

> I see my allergies and symptoms as friends/guides to keep me in tune with myself and on my path of health and growth. It is an ongoing process. This is a beginning, not an end.

14 Multiple Sclerosis: An Example of our Approach

This chapter concerns a specific ailment, Multiple Sclerosis, since over the years we have had particular experience of working with people with this diagnosis. However, we think that our remarks about MS also illustrate principles that will be useful in understanding and responding to many disease processes. Much can be learned in this chapter that may apply, for example, to cancer, cardiovascular disease, arthritis, and numerous other difficult medical conditions.

The Disease Description

Multiple sclerosis (disseminated sclerosis, MS) is a chronic disorder of the nervous system, typically affecting young and middle aged adults. Although its causes are uncertain, there are suggestions of inherited susceptibility as well as environmental and infectious factors. The disease may be related to auto-immune damage, triggered by a slow virus or other infection. In any case, once the disease is active, the myelin sheaths surrounding the nerves in the brain and spinal cord become damaged, leaving fibrous scarring in hardened (sclerosed) patches; this damage can be widely scattered through the nervous system.

There is a wide variety of clinical nervous system signs and symptoms, which are well documented in the medical literature. The disease is prone to relapses and remissions. In the early stages, common symptoms are limb weakness and heaviness, blurred or double vision in one or both eyes, tingling and numbness in a limb or in the trunk, vertigo, and unsteadiness or poor balance in walking. The bladder can be affected, causing frequency, urgency or difficulty passing water. The first attack often clears up completely within a few months; often there is a recurrence within two years. Some people continue to recover after relapses; others enter a progressive stage, with weakness and deterioration continuing. As well as increasing motor disability, there may be urinary retention or incontinence, slurred speech, and mental changes with emotional lability, depression or euphoria. No definitive curative treatment is known. Prescribed drugs can sometimes help the immediate episode, and recent evidence indicates that for some they may also improve the long-term outlook.

Our Observations

In the more than 40 years that we led experiential programs together, we met and worked with dozens of people with the diagnosis of MS. During that time, we built up some impressions about this disease process, and the people who suffer with it, and came to identify a broad personality profile of these people.

In general, the people we worked with had a high need for control in their lives. They were often much above average in intelligence. Frequently, they were goal oriented achievers, with consequently high degrees of self-hate (such as we described in Chapter 1). Lurking under an apparent independence there was commonly a profoundly held victim stance; these people had often become ferociously independent in an attempt to compensate for their underlying interpretation that they were being controlled by others in their lives. They often procrastinated; they had a difficult time translating thought into action. They were good talkers, and made lots of plans; however, they became (sometimes literally) paralysed when faced with the challenge of putting their dreams into action. Although some of them had been athletic in earlier times, they commonly experienced a progressive weakness, often accompanied by muscle tightness and shaking.

Through the years, we asked all the clients we saw with MS to provide a summary of their perspectives on their illness process; indeed, we made similar requests to people with other illness profiles too. Whereas people with allergies and phobias and chronic fatigue syndrome were very eager to provide us with summaries of their personal learnings about illness patterns, the people with MS were distinctly reluctant to respond. So, in all these years, only a few people provided the requested documentation. Hence, the quotations in this article come from interviewing people, and asking pointed questions, as well as from the few written accounts we received.

We found a remarkable sex difference in how people facing MS dealt with information provided to them. For both men and women suffering with MS, the work and learning inevitably centred around their isolation, their high need for control, and their abandonment of their bodies. We believe we treated people of both sexes in the same manner in our programs. However, when they were given breathing exercises, and invited to engage in dialogue with friends, women were generally much more likely to follow our advice. Women seemed to have more perseverance, and willingness to face themselves. They would dedicate themselves to breathing, relating, and working through the process; men, on the other hand, often seemed to sink back and give up. As a result, women were generally more solid in their healing than men. The men commonly protested that it was too difficult to follow a routine regimen of breathing; while the men resisted, the women just got down to work and applied themselves to the exercises. Perhaps this was the expression of greater endurance and perseverance on the women's part; on the negative side, perhaps they were simply better at complying with instructions. One professional woman with the diagnosis of MS said the following:

> A woman is closer to her body than a man; hence a woman will be able to find her way into her body better than a man. Women have had experiences with childbirth and menstruation, and are more familiar with the general experience of their bodies; they know their bodies a little, and are more ready to live in them. A man has never known his body except as a tool or as a function, and has a difficult time finding his way home.

One man learned to walk without his cane when he had the stimulation of being in a program; when he returned home, however, he did not continue his exercise and went back to a wheel chair. A woman from the same city sold her wheelchair to acquire the funds to attend an additional residential program; when her healing became her purpose, she quickly came into health, and remained so after she returned home.

In the remainder of this chapter, we look more closely at some of the most common themes we observed in these people. We believe that there are connections to be made between these themes and the MS illness process, and indeed to other illnesses.

Blame

The people we worked with were often invested in blame, either blaming themselves for getting the illness, or blaming some external factor (parents, for example, or some infectious agent). We believe this blame served to cement the illness process, and indeed was a factor in it; in our experience, blame operates against symptom improvement. One woman devoted a great deal of energy at the beginning of her program to complaining about how handicapped people were not being adequately considered in this mixed group of people; she politicized the situation, instead of working on her own capabilities. When she was wrapped up in this, she did not have time or energy left to investigate her own relationship to the disease process. We observed that as long as the victim/blame stance persists, the MS process also persists. People often confuse personal responsibility with self-blame so that when they start trying to be accountable, they often shift from a victim stance into blaming themselves for what has happened. One MS client said:

> I knew I was responsible for being sick, but I thought that it was just stupidity. I had allowed my defences to drop, and I got sick from an external agent. It was my bad luck to get MS rather than the flu. There was nothing I could do when the external agent had attacked.

We believe that healing is facilitated when people distinguish clearly between self-blame/victimhood and personal responsibility, and have discussed this difference more fully in Chapter 3.

Isolation

As long as people are stuck in fault-finding, they fail to see beyond their own version of the world. Hence, they are kept from genuine dialogue. They perpetuate their isolation where they are trapped, and they seem unable to find the healing that would come with personal responsibility and interpersonal dialogue. These comments illustrate:

> I withdraw into myself when things get tough. I learned early to confide only in myself.

> Not needing help got distorted into helplessness. The last people that I would confide in were my parents. The logical extension was withdrawal.

Willfulness

We propose that MS frequently involves a misuse of the will. Rather than using their will and determination to follow through with a plan, the people we worked with often used their will as a defensive "willfulness" and resistance. Willful people force themselves through life, and sometimes the only way they can relax is to acquire an illness condition that makes them rest. Often, they are driven to fulfil obligations to others, and become embroiled in the self-hate cycle we described in Chapter 1. When the people we worked with attempted to become responsible for their illness, they frequently tried to will themselves into wellness, which further fixated the MS process. There is a difference between willfulness and will. This statement is pertinent:

> I did not want to use my will power, since it produced more pain. I didn't really believe that anything could change.

High Achievers

As we have said, the people we worked with around MS were often high achievers, with all the difficulties associated with a life attitude of striving, self-denial and self-discontent. They were driven:

> *I had to be great.*

> *With this high achievement, I always felt inadequate. I could not choose what to do, since the risk of choosing poorly and not keeping great was too great.*

> *I don't know when to stop.*

Since so many of these people were over-achievers, we began to wonder if MS was providing them a way to rest that the person could not otherwise accept. Literally, they had to be struck down in order to accept rest and help from others.

Misunderstood

The personal histories of the people we worked with often involved strong achievement ethics, accompanied by the loneliness that came with believing that they were misunderstood. One young man, whose parents were in academia, said:

> *I had to be self-reliant. In my relationships with my parents, I felt like I was in a university lecture; I never felt understood, and to them, my pain and sadness were not important... I was told to "buckle down" and be a little stronger.*

We came to know this young man's parents, and discovered that their view was quite different from his. Based on our experience of his mother, we believed that she did in fact care about his pain and sadness. Perhaps this young man's MS was related to his particular vision, in which he believed that he was unloved, and was expected to achieve. The problem was not with the parenting as such, but with the individual's experience of the parenting.

Mental Correlates

We frequently observed amongst the MS sufferers we met a distinctive mental lassitude that accompanied their muscular weakness. Previously productive people became very undirected, with only occasional episodes of vitality:

I lived in a semivegetative state with odd bursts of excitement.

I was full of self defeating behaviour, never completing anything. When I didn't complete anything then I couldn't be judged, and I had an excuse. Underlying this is a fear of failure, or of being condemned.

My decision making has been poor. I have a paralysis of action. There is a split between thought and action. Thought is not translated into action. My whole life feels paralysed.

In at least one of the cases we have seen, there was evidence of an underlying mental disorganization. This particular young woman kept her body tight, and stiffly went through her days as a manager. She was in control of herself, and in control of the business she managed. However, inside, she was a frightened child who was afraid of going crazy. When she finally gave in and shared her panic and anxiety, she drew closer to her life partner, and the symptoms of MS subsided. She had to share her fear of going crazy; she had experienced a craziness in other members of her family, and she was keeping herself in stern control to keep herself from flying away, or disintegrating into madness.

Self-Hate

In the clients we met, a self-hate process often interfered with the self-awareness that might lead to healing:

I've been afraid to look at myself – because when I did, I turned it against myself. Whatever I found about myself I used for self-blame.

The people we worked with became frustrated in never being perfect, even though they attempted very large tasks. Thus, even though they often accomplished a great deal, they didn't reap the fruits of their labours, often succumbing instead to self-hate for falling short of their grandiose expectations of themselves.

Work hard enough, with enough will power, and you can do anything – that's what I thought. The result was that I was never great at anything. People would always do better than me. I compared myself to the encyclopedic 19th-century writers, and always came up wanting.

Procrastination

Mixed in with a strong achievement ethic was a common tendency to procrastinate. We think especially of one woman who became fascinated with her illness process, and indeed learned to have the symptoms of muscular weakness turn around inside of minutes with dedicated breathing. She applied to graduate school, and intended to write up her experiences with MS as a doctoral dissertation. For years she obsessed about the thesis, and could not get down to writing it, even though she had the information at hand that she was ready to synthesize. At the time of our writing the 1998 edition of this book, she had still not finished the dissertation for her Ph.D. Since then, we have learned that she eventually completed it through a non-traditional school, and that her MS is now in abeyance.

The people we worked with were often exceptionally intelligent. They sometimes tended towards idealistic dreaming, rather than dedicating themselves to practical pursuits. Thus, they would fantasize and procrastinate, and not engage themselves fully in their lives. They often came to understand their illness process very well, without doing anything about it. They knew what they should do; but, it seemed that they would rather think about it than do it. Their capability to rationalize was very marked. They were like a powerful automobile with the transmission disengaged – they couldn't seem to get into gear! This same process seemed also to show in their muscular weakness: they were very capable physically, but often did not engage their strength.

> My character is basically flawed. I am intelligent, but the flaw prevents me from using my intelligence in the real world. I succumb to gross absurd self-idealizations as a substitute for actions.

Procrastination and idealistic dreaming seemed to replace physical engagement and incarnation. There seemed to be a failure to translate idea into action. They abandoned their bodies, to take up residence in the dream states of their minds.

Disembodiment

We see MS as a disease of disembodiment. The people we met were often afraid of their passions, and reluctant to surrender to the energies that flowed through them. Often, they were uncomfortable with their sexuality. Their bodies tightened as they exerted increasing control over their feelings and expression, through repression and self-denial. They seemed to be leaving their bodies, and living predominantly in their minds.

In MS, the body is largely denied. Often, it is experienced as a tool, rather than a source of pleasure or any other sensation. Sensations of many kinds are ignored, and sexual inhibitions are often hidden in their symptoms. For people with MS, therefore, healing involves incarnation. In this process, people often will show fears of intimacy, and discomfort with sexuality in specific, and sensations in general. One young woman did not want to shake (which often occurs with deep breathing), because she thought this was "gross." In the Chinese medicine theory of the Five Stages of Change, MS is a disease of the earth, involving a difficulty with fully incarnating, being present and in the flesh. This is seen in Chinese medicine to be accompanied by a disturbance of *yi* (purpose or intention). As facets of this earth imbalance, there are related disturbances in boundaries and in relationships.

The people we worked with had trouble experiencing their bodies as their own. Rather they tended to see themselves as the victims of a disease process that had taken over. Indeed, the disease was sometimes portrayed as a devil inhabiting the body. One woman in her forties struggled to take charge of her process, and was learning to breathe to relax her tight muscles. She had previously been unable to shop, for example, since her body would seize into painful contractions after she had visited a couple of stores in a shopping centre. After her dedication to breathing, she learned to accept the tightness that would come when she breathed; it was as if some internal devil was fighting her attempt to relax. She would breathe through the tightness, and her muscles would relax again. Her triumph came when she walked several miles around the lake at the family cottage; for years prior to this time, she could scarcely enjoy even a brief walk in nature, since her body would seize up. Coming to attend a program was an act of self determination and self-definition. Her disease process was attempting to prevent her from improving, by making her tight and tired. A typical comment:

I was out of my body.

This woman discovered that her tightness was not random. She would contract when she was not expressing her feelings. In particular, she had shut down her sexuality, and she discovered in an educational program that she would tighten up around attractive young men. When she learned to express her attractions to these young men (without any intention to act on these attractions), she began to feel more free with the feelings, and her symptoms subsided. A similar easement came as she learned to express her anger in a more open and direct fashion. She had previously used a "nice" mask to cover her feelings (she herself often didn't know when she was displeased); when she learned to identify her negative feelings, and express them, her symptoms declined remarkably. So, MS can be seen as a consequence of limited expression, arising from a fear to accept and live with one's passions. One begins to heal when the sensations and pleasures of the body are accepted:

I'm now doing things I haven't done since I was seventeen years old.

Control

The people we worked with were generally afraid to be out of control. Hence, they tended to keep their symptoms secret, and were reluctant to talk about the fears they had when they experienced muscular weakness, or a decline in vision. They struggled to maintain an image to others as being in control, and needing no one. Hence, they were often in positions of responsibility, and looked very capable. Their fears and suffering were kept private. Consequently, they did not experience the comfort that could come in sharing their feelings and experience with a friend or co-worker. They were isolated, and tended to want to take care of everything themselves.

We have found that MS frequently involves issues of domination/submission and surrender (as we define these terms in Chapter 3). Strongly controlled and controlling, people with the disease seemed to hold their bodies in a rigid fashion, and will themselves (and others) through life. They submitted only reluctantly to authority, and often resisted in passive ways when they must submit. They could be cruel to themselves in their dominance of their own physical and mental being. They tended to use their bodies rather than inhabiting or feeling them. We noticed that such a rigid body armouring is usually held in place by severely limited breathing. In a fundamental way, they were not in their bodies, and needed to learn to reinhabit their physical being through a process of surrender. When these people learned to breathe more deeply, their symptoms (which they often hated) tended to exacerbate. They shook more, and they sometimes experienced panic or anxiety. They tended to want to tighten up again, to resist the symptoms, and in this way fight the expression of feeling and energy that accompanied more breathing. When they contracted and resisted, they were in a mode of submission to their symptoms, which had taken over and dominated their lives. If they persisted in breathing, however, and surrendered to the release that would come, their muscular strength often returned, and they would find more energy for physical activity. They frequently found this frightening, as they were beginning to inhabit the bodies that they had previously abandoned. Their temptation was to submit to the symptoms of tightness and disincarnation, rather than surrender to their feelings.

Often, they reported that they were afraid of the shaking that came with breathing practice, because it represented a loss of control to them; we encouraged them to let go, to surrender to the body's natural responses, and relax. They were often embarrassed to shake when other people were present; when they learned to share this shaking instead of hiding it, they were already well into the process of surrender.

Caretaking

A frequent theme was that of being a caretaker. In relationships, people we knew with MS often smoothed the waters, and took care of others. In several instances, they saw it as their duty as children to take care of one or both of their parents.

When people have lived all their lives as a caretaker, sometimes it seems that the only way they can relax is to become ill themselves, and then have someone take care of them. Perhaps the mental framework of seeing relationships as caretaking is a feature of the MS process. These people were not connecting; instead, relationships were largely seen in terms of taking care of others, or being taken care of themselves. In one case, a grown man discovered that his mother who had provided a lot of his care wanted to move from his home town; when he was unhappy about this, she did not move, because she was afraid that his symptoms would get worse. She didn't tell him this directly, only talked to her friends about it. This illustrates the failure of dialogue, wherein the mother objectified the son as unable to face these issues directly. She was afraid he would get sicker if she moved away; in this sense, she believed his health was under her control. She was martyred to his illness, and the rest of his family and friends got caught up in the victim attitude and accompanying objectification. Thus the mother limited herself, and in this way submitted to her son's control demands, thus permitting him to avoid the anxiety he had around possibly having her more distant geographically.

Pleasing

We found that people with MS were often overly nice in their demeanour. Their desire to be liked and accepted gave them an accommodating air, and a consistently reasonable, placating quality. They were so afraid to be rejected that they tried desperately to please others. Often they had been "good children," pleasing their parents, and they had grown up to be adults who fit in. Thus, they denied their own passions, and were afraid to express anger or negative feelings. They kept themselves (and others) under control by limiting the expression of negative feelings.

They tended to be political rather than personal (see Chapter 3 for this more on this distinction), favouring control over vulnerability. They would talk about how things should be, and what was wrong with society, or other people; they often did this in a very cool, cerebral fashion. Inside they were often very angry (at their spouses or family, or at the disease itself); but they converted this anger into political discussions, rather than express it directly.

Limited Vision

MS can be seen as involving a limited vision. We noted that a frequent theme amongst these clients was a refusal to see that they could take more responsibility for their illness process. For example, we generally recommend that people who are suffering from chronic or severe illnesses should breathe in a concentrated fashion as much as possible – as much as fifteen minutes four times per day. Also, we recommend to people with MS that they get some regular exercise to encourage their muscles to move in a synchronized fashion. Often, we suggest that people go the gymnasium to build up muscular tone, or embark upon walking or calisthenics.

Rather than put these suggestions into practice, we found that many sought answers and advice from an authority or a guru; they seemed to prefer someone else's reframing over taking the courage to find the meaning of the disease state in themselves. In this limited, field-dependent vision, people continued to be filled with self-hate, striving to live up to someone else's suggestions (parents, healers, gurus, etc.) instead of meeting the challenge of facing life for themselves and making up their own minds about things. Often, these very intelligent, capable people had a long history of subjugating themselves to teachers and authorities. We met numerous people who would rather look for another guru who could tell them how to become spiritually enlightened, rather than face up to the messy day-to-day task of coming into their bodies through breathing and personal responsibility.

Healing Through Revision

What would facilitate a healing is a "revision" – literally, coming to see with original eyes what comes from inside. Some of the people we worked with had previously had such a self-directed vision, and lost it; others had perhaps never developed the ability to "see" for themselves. Thus, they were sick due to limited vision. Their healing involved an updating or revisioning of their self-concept and their attitudes about others. Commonly, parents, authority figures and self had all been objectified; they would appear very different with updated perspectives. This revision takes courage, and when people fail in courage, they succumb instead to self-hate. A note from one courageous person:

I am my disease. This has been a total revolution in thinking from where I was at. I am now open to change things. I could still have MS. My patterns in life were the disease. All I had to do was change my life, and I would not be sick.

Often, desperation brought the person to the brink of self-discovery:

The paralysis was increasing, and I was having increasing difficulty translating my thoughts into actions. My right side was paralysed for two weeks. I believed that it was just a matter of time, and I was scared. I couldn't walk, and I had to radically change my life.

As in many illness processes, a common nuclear problem involved fixated attitudinal positions. Healing often progressed when people recognized their participation in the illness process. One man said.

The assumptions that I was holding were dead ends. I could not heal because my body was fixed, and was basically a container. I used the "cash register approach" to life — I collected experiences and rang them up. I thought if I could collect enough experiences I could change.

When they came to a new attitude, wherein they could learn about the illness and take responsibility for it, the healing could progress:

On the advice of my friends, I realized that I could do something. I now realize that I wasn't a victim.

Different ways of thinking about energy can be very useful in working with MS. Previously, a client had believed that he was running out of energy, and that his physical body which generated and stored the energy was failing. Then he began to see in terms of the Chinese acupuncture theory, where energy is universally abundant, and is merely blocked or fixated in illness states. As he began to become interested in unfixating the energy (through breathing, and open dialogues with significant others), he began to feel more energetic:

I have a new perspective. I believe in the energy body; the energy body and I are constantly in flux, in transformation.

Acupuncture, and other energy approaches can be very helpful:

I am actually being transformed after needles. You still recognize me because enough of the old pattern persists.

To work effectively with the illness process, the practitioner can be a friend as well as a professional, while still maintaining appropriate boundaries. Helpers can establish relationships in which clients can learn without the harshness of their oppressive superego. They will often express a feeling of gratitude that someone reached out, and appreciated them, even when they were not accepting themselves:

You accepted me as a friend.

Awareness Into Action

With awareness, people with MS can learn not to give in to the tendency to disengage. Instead, they can engage with life, and move ahead with healthier, more active perspectives. Much improvement comes with the ability to laugh:

I don't have to succumb to this flaw. Now, for the first time in my life, I'm happy. I can take responsibility for myself. Now, I can laugh at myself, and not take my idealizations and superego so seriously.

As they become more aware of the themes that run through their illness process, they can learn to understand and take more responsibility for themselves. Generally, they will acknowledge that they knew that their illness would wax and wane in relation to their attitudes and life experiences:

Deep down, I knew all along what was going on.

A New Attitude

When people come to see their illness process as an expression of themselves, they need no longer do battle with themselves and the disease. They can become engaged in a learning process, wherein they come to accept and appreciate the meaning of their illness process. We believe this is true of many disease processes, not just MS. Some comments:

I'm more curious than afraid now.

My plan now is to listen to my superego, and then go about my own business. Getting MS has been a blessing in disguise. I have been learning to appreciate my symptoms.

We believe that healing from MS involves a change in relationship with self, others and the world:

When I interact with anyone, I become different. Relationships heal. The healing process is in interaction.

People's symptoms often improve when they come to see their disease process as a learning opportunity, rather than an illness that they have acquired. They become interested in their personality configuration, and come to see more and more how their attitudes and actions determine the course of their illness:

Understanding the patterns led to these awarenesses.

They become less intent upon the final outcome of being disease free, and become more interested in learning about the process itself:

The symptoms I still have will slowly recede.

People can gradually come to think of themselves in a new way, where they no longer equate themselves with their disease, but rather see themselves as persons involved in a life process:

It's been a phenomenal experience realizing I don't have to be sick.

I no longer have MS. My neurologist, however, has a different assumption system; he thinks I still have it, in remission.

Recommendations

In summary, we recommend the following in learning to deal effectively with the issues relating to Multiple Sclerosis:

- Learn about the victim stance, accept it, and take responsibility for it.

- Even if one is afraid, take the courage to take action, rather than sitting back from life.

- Breathe! Symptoms will often regress with routine breathing. Clients feel increased strength and vitality after breathing, though they also feel more anxious and exposed.

- People with MS have abandoned their bodies, and have thus avoided experiencing their feelings (thus limiting their sexual expression, and their creativity). Learn to come home into the body.

- Interacting meaningfully with others in open honest communication, owning objectifications, and not succumbing to them – this is the path to healing through dialogue.

- Learn to accept instability, insecurity and shaking.

- Express anger, and other uncomfortable feelings, more directly. In this way, the feelings will not be stuck in the body, and the tightness will gradually recede.

A Radical Thought

The prognosis in MS is extremely variable; even the most severe cases can have sudden deterioration followed by striking improvement. So, when someone improves, it is difficult to assess what is the normal course of the ebb and flow of the disease, and what is the result of some beneficial activity or treatment. Our radical hypothesis is this – perhaps the disease itself does not wax and wane, but instead maybe it reflects changes in the person on other levels that express themselves as symptomatic improvements or deteriorations.

We have seen numerous people make some very strong and enduring changes in their lives, with a marked lessening of their symptoms. With some, the improvement has been so dramatic that they seem to be free of disease. Conventional medical thinking suggests that the lesions are still there, but are somehow quiescent. We wonder if the lesions of the central nervous system can somehow vanish. In other words, is the disease necessarily always there? We have seen an upgoing plantar response (a medical diagnostic test; scratching the sole of the foot elicits a spontaneous response in the toes. Normally the big toe will go down when the nerve tracts are intact; an upgoing toe is evidence of central nervous system dysfunction) change to a downgoing normal response after one episode of body work. Perhaps the lesions are altered when these people breathe and inhabit themselves. If this were so, we would be challenged to re-think many of our assumptions about other serious illnesses, such as cancer and heart disease, and the supposed inevitability of the biological processes that underlie them.

15 Disengaging Depression

Many people experience depression at some time in their lives. For some, depression is a chronic, crippling fact that dims the enjoyment of life. Others experience episodes of depression related to different circumstances in their lives. Over the years, we have met and worked with many people who have successfully wrestled with these processes, and their courage and learning have helped us in our understanding of this common problem.

While depression takes many forms, we see that common elements in these variations include an inner stuckness and symptoms associated with restricted life energy. Depression comes with the inhibition of life.

Whether people experience depression as a constant in their lives or have episodes of depression punctuated with periods of relief, depression appears to involve a contraction of life energy. Depressed people lose interest in what previously had much meaning, whether it be a job, a partner, family members, recreational activities, social functions, or participation in social affairs such as church or school. They might echo the words of Shakespeare's Hamlet: "O God! O God! How weary, stale, flat, and unprofitable seem to me all the uses of this world."

In these people's world, there is little joy, no spontaneity, a flattening of feelings, a gloomy pall on all experience, a loss of hope and optimism, a strong sense of isolation, difficulty in finding meaning and a chronic state of boredom. Their energy level is low, so all tasks appear to be enormous, impossible or not worth the effort. Frequently, sleep disturbances dominate – perhaps being unable to sleep, or awakening early and being unable to return to sleep, or maybe wishing to sleep all the time. Sometimes, this is accompanied by compensatory mechanisms such as eating disorders (with either extreme loss or gain in weight) or an increased amount of addictive behaviour. The overall effect is a progressive withdrawal from life.

Our basic position is that depression is a symptom of energy fixation. When people are withheld, not flowing in their lives, they are prone to the stuckness which is often labeled "depression."

Sadness and Letting Go: Western and Chinese Perspectives

Sadness and depression are different. Sadness is a feeling among others that come and go in a person's life, related to different situations. The feeling of sadness is normal and healthy, and indeed provides for depth and richness of life experience. One can feel very alive in experiencing sadness.

Depression occurs when life energy is somehow fixated, or inhibited from expression; then the vitality of the individual's life is blunted.

In the Chinese Five Stages of Change, images of the cycle of the seasons illustrate the healthy movement and flow of life. Feelings are to a person's inner world what temperature variations are to the external world. Just as there are cycles of heat changes in the outer environment, so there are cycles of shifting feelings and moods within. The heat and brightness of summer correspond to the expansive warmth and optimism of joy. The damp coolness and crispness of winter correspond to the isolation and the storage of feelings in a contracted state. Just as the spring is filled with fresh growth and eruption of new life forms, so is the inner world of a person full of anticipation, hope, movement and sometimes aggression. In the fall, as resources are being collected for the ensuing year's growth, there is a sadness in the air. This is similar to the sadness within people that is so natural and sweet, providing the experience of depth and felt meaning.

The inner cyclical seasons of sadness are unique to each individual. Personal growth and development involve a continuing series of new achievements, while letting go of older acquisitions. It is those episodes of letting go that are accompanied by feelings of sadness – the feeling of sadness is organic, existential and inevitable. Just as the mood of the seasons changes with the quietude of fall becoming the buoyancy of spring, so people's feelings will transform, bringing re-invigoration – into action, meaningfulness and shifts of growth – unless the individual loses faith (as we describe it in Chapter 3), becomes neurotically anxious and wants to hang on. When people lose faith, they commonly lay the ground for the future development of depression.

The necessity of letting go described in these images from Chinese medicine is also recognized in Western psychological thought. For some, the roots of depression can be found in failures to fully experience and let go of inevitable losses in early childhood experience.

Psychoanalyst Melanie Klein, for example, saw the necessity of letting go as "the central position in the child's development," leading to an ubiquitous "infantile depressive position." The accompanying "pining" for the lost love object (in the first instance, the mother) must be "worked through and gradually overcome," she said, in order to accomplish integrative growth.[1] Sadness is a natural experience that accompanies the experiences of letting go. To the extent that people do not accomplish this letting go, they become more prone to depression. Judith Viorst's very readable book *Necessary Losses* explores and extends this theme.[2]

Looking to a person's childhood to find the roots of depression in adulthood can provide important insight. However, there is also a danger in doing so that people might blame their childhoods, or their parents, or their own past failings, for their current predicament. In effect, they make themselves victims of their past experiences. Whereas the responsible expression of feelings related to the past can help people move forward in their lives (see Chapter 11), becoming fixated in blame is likely to make matters worse. As we discussed in Chapter 2, blame is characteristic of a power-based approach to one's life. We recommend instead that people develop their capacity for strength and a self-responsible approach to both their past and present experience. As Judith Viorst's book makes clear, there are opportunities throughout one's life, not just in childhood, to practice letting go.

An Educational Perspective on Depression

In our work, we have developed an educational rather than a therapeutic approach to a wide range of life issues, including depression. We discuss the distinction between education and therapy in Chapter 18. Therapeutically, carefully prescribed medications may be helpful in the short term, though they are often accompanied by side effects and an eventual decline in efficacy. From an educational perspective, it is possible for people to understand and take charge of their own pattern of depression, no matter how organic or otherwise its origins may appear to be. In our experience, most depressed persons can benefit from coming to terms with the internal process of depression creation. They can learn about themselves and their life style choices, and discover their own participation in the process of depression. With such a self-responsible attitude, people have greater possibilities for choosing for themselves more appropriate solutions to their life issues. When they share this process with friends and loved ones, they are on the way to healing. Withholding inclines one's energy to depression; mobilization of feelings, contact, sharing and expression all contribute to keeping the process of one's life vibrant and responsive.

The information and ideas that follow are intended to contribute to such an educational process and should be helpful both to people experiencing depression and practitioners who work with them.

Two Broad Categories of Depression

Besides the so-called "reactive depression" that sometimes arises in response to an external event, such as the death of a family member, there are depressions that are rooted in early psychological development. In our work over the years with a wide variety of people, we have found it useful to conceptualize two broad categories of depression originating in earlier years. These are depressions with clear roots in childhood deprivation ("anaclitic" depressions) and depressions arising from the long-term process of self-hate we described in Chapter 1. In our experience, by far the most frequent of these is self-hating depression. Indeed, since the process of self-hate is to some degree or other a universal experience, there are probably elements of self-hating in all forms of depression. While the distinction between these two categories can be very useful, both for practitioners and people dealing with depression themselves, it is important to bear in mind that the two are not mutually exclusive; often a person will experience a combination of the two.

Self-Hate Depression

This kind of depression is a result of a self-perpetuating cycle of feeling bad about one's self for having abandoned one's true nature in order to strive towards an ideal. Further self-hate occurs when the goal of perfection proves impossible. We describe this process in detail in Chapter 1. From a psychoanalytic perspective, a relentlessly punitive superego is punishing the ego for desiring the expression of unacceptable impulses (including the impulse to abandon the self). People who experience severe depression of this sort tend to loathe themselves, believing they should be punished. Sometimes, being kind to a person dominated by this kind of self-directed loathing and anger only makes matters worse. In face of kindness and understanding, these people tend to further hate themselves for what they see as having duped anyone offering kindness; believing that kindness must be reserved for worthy individuals, their inner sense of unworthiness dictates that they be further punished. Thus, kindness and understanding can aggravate the depression, rather than help to alleviate it.

When people want to work through a self-hating depression we encourage them to pay attention to incomplete experiences or "gestalts," with a focus on feelings (both positive and negative) that they have previously not expressed. For many people, prominent among these will be grief and anger, which are often closely linked. Incomplete grieving entails the withholding of feelings, including anger. Anger may then be turned against the self. This self-aggression can become a central element of the depression process, progressing in extreme cases to suicide. We say more about this aspect of the self-hating cycle below, under the heading When People Lose Loved Ones.

When people find healthy ways to express feelings, including but not limited to grief and anger, they can begin to release the fixations of energy that often lead to depression. With courage and curiosity, people can interrupt the self-hating cycle. Breathing and the five A's we outlined in Chapter 1 – awareness, acknowledgement, acceptance, action and appreciation – can be of enormous help in this process.

When people learn to share with others and responsibly express feelings they have previously held back, their depression will often shift. So, as we frequently advise, contact and sharing are key elements in keeping one's energy alive and moving. When the energy of life is moving, depression does not fixate.

Deprived Childhoods (Anaclitic Depression)

Some infants and children are offered very little emotional and physical stimulation in their early years. Others seem unable to accept what emotional and physical stimulation is provided by their caretakers. As with plants that will go to seed when lacking the essential ingredients of sun and rain, these children tend to contract and withdraw behind a shell-like wall to protect themselves. Lacking this early vigorous growth creates a handicap that these people will carry on into adulthood. Such a "failure-to-thrive" child will likely grow into a "failure-to-thrive" adult who is lacking in energy, expansiveness, enthusiasm, spontaneity, resilience and psychological robustness.

We believe that, fundamentally, people are always connected to one another and to all of the universe. However, individuals do not always feel that connection and often experience themselves as profoundly isolated and alone. Indeed, existentialists propose that life and growth are inevitably accompanied by anxiety. Filled with such anxiety, the child faces one of life's earliest and most important decisions – to bond or withdraw. If the caretaker provides adequate stimulation appropriate for that child, there is a positive attraction towards establishing an experienced sense of bonding. We do not think that children need "love," but rather, they require the particular form of stimulation that is uniquely desired by the child. This may help explain the lack of apparent bonding in some "failure-to-thrive" children when other children bond healthily with the same caretaker, who offers the same quality of parental care and stimulation to all of them.

This failure-to-thrive form of depression has been labeled "anaclitic," meaning relating to emotional dependency and lack of nourishment. In contemporary medicine, it is sometimes diagnosed as Reactive Attachment Disorder or RAD. Some such people manage to achieve at least superficially effective relationships and employment, but their desolate core structure nevertheless presents them with enormous difficulty in the task of living fulfilling lives. Commonly, these people describe their feelings in terms of "emptiness," "shallowness" or "hollowness," lacking excitement and joy. Sometimes, to avoid this emptiness, they become involved in substance abuse in an attempt to experience some "highs" in life, even if they must pay later with ensuing equivalent "lows." The highs provide the simulacrum of aliveness.

The issues in anaclitic depression can thus be very difficult for the sufferer. Since the effects of early deprivation are so panoramic and pervasive, these individuals often require therapy and counselling to begin to deal with their depressive situation. Along the way, as they learn to trust their professional helper, they can begin to open up and receive what they did not get as children. Sometimes, this will involve a kind of re-parenting.

In this process they can begin to receive and appreciate the stimulation of another's feelings. Being taken care of is not enough. Instead, they are in need of an authentic, personal, dialogical contact. The self that has been in hiding requires a reason to stir and come forward beyond its own walls.

Eventually, these people can face the challenge of moving beyond therapeutic dependency by creating a life style for themselves that fosters caring, support and stimulation. What they did not have as children, they can learn to find and enjoy in adulthood. Through responsible communication, and being willing to open up and share in a vulnerable, open way, they can create and maintain an atmosphere wherein they can learn and grow. Programs at The Haven have been helpful for many who are overcoming the effects of early deprivation. As people learn to establish relationships of mutual support and caring, they can gradually move themselves through and beyond their depression. This is what Joann Peterson meant by Disengaging Depression, the name of a program she developed with Linda Nicholls and Judy Lemon and led at The Haven for many years.[3] The antidote to depression – of all sorts – is a deepening intimacy with others.

Differentiating the Types of Depression

Ambivalence is a core issue that can help differentiate between these two categories of depression. The anaclitically depressed person is convinced of the inadvisability of investing feelings in others; past experiences with people have been unsatisfactory, possibly hurtful or dangerous. Thus, there is little or no ambivalence in anaclitically depressed people; they are deeply convinced that contact is unwise. If the origin of a person's depression is inadequate psychological and emotional nourishment, what is needed first of all is a form of re-parenting, or providing the emotional sustenance and stimulation that was lacking in childhood. Only once this is achieved will the person be ready to embark on the journey to a fuller experience of self and connection with others.

Self-hating depressed people on the other hand often experience a great deal of ambivalence. Frequently, they have been deeply involved with others, but have been confused by a wide incongruence of experiences, positive and negative. A typical scenario would involve a child with a strong attachment to a parent who is unstable or emotionally unpredictable and ambivalent in their attitude to the child. Another situation might involve superficially "sweet" parents who forbid the expression of negative feelings, whether their own or their children's. When the children experience negative feelings in themselves, they find nowhere to direct them except against themselves. A healthier environment – and one which can be created later in life – would allow regular expression and clearing of these ambivalent feelings, thus minimizing the tendency to self-hate depression. If the origin of the depression is harsh self-criticism and self-hate, the person needs to establish contact through direct mirroring and feedback and responsible communication.

Thus, these two categories of depression call for different responses. The kind of emotional support that is important for the person mired in an anaclitic depression is generally ineffective with those wrestling with a depression involving self-hate; indeed, as we have seen, such an approach may contribute to worsening the situation. Unfortunately, many times, processes of depression involve a combination of these two broad types, necessitating a shifting of attitude and approaches over time. Nevertheless, most people will benefit from empathy and understanding, which can afford them a broadened perspective and a growing sense of self-compassion and acceptance.

When People Lose Loved Ones

When relatively healthy, autonomous people lose a loved one through a separation for any reason (for example, divorce, death, or children leaving home), they are likely to experience the sadness of missing the other. Very commonly, however, relationships have been more embroiled with ambivalence and unexpressed emotional transactions ("incomplete gestalts"); the people involved have failed to differentiate into autonomous beings. Sometimes, they may appear on the surface to be ideal – never arguing, always being reasonable and logical, perhaps even appearing to take good care of one another. Although they have been deeply involved with one another, much has been repressed. At the time of a separation, they may experience sadness in relation to the positive feelings they had. However, the unexpressed negative feelings produce a serious complication. Sometimes these can be directed outwardly as an anger against the world, or as a blaming and rejection of others. More often, people direct the unexpressed negative feelings against themselves, giving rise to the symptoms of depression. As we have seen, common features of this depression are low energy, lack of motivation and inability to feel and express emotions. Life is blunted, flattened.

When the self-directed hostility is denied or ignored, the depressive process grows underground. Frequently, it finds expression, through a process of somatization, in a myriad of physical symptoms (including headaches, digestive problems, weakness and lassitude). We agree with the notion that this can progress to be a feature of diagnosable illnesses, including arthritis, cardiovascular disorders and cancer. Other common directions of expression are in obsessive and addictive behaviours (connected with work, substances, food, or people), allergies and phobias, difficulties at work or in relationships, a variety of disturbances (for example, learning, sleep, or eating), loss of sexual desire, and a general state of boredom. Without taking appropriate action, these can develop into full scale clinical depressions.

As we have seen, the task for people who want to move through this kind of depression is to pay attention to incomplete gestalts, unfinished business and unexpressed feelings and thoughts. Programs such as are offered at The Haven can help with this, as can ongoing connection and intimacy with others.

Cyclical Depressions

Currently, much attention has been given to a commonly diagnosed group of depressive syndromes that are described as being "cyclical." The most severe form is identified as a manic-depressive or bipolar syndrome. Current thinking holds that these cyclical depressions are primarily genetically and organically determined; thus, they are treated almost exclusively with medications. Often the manic phase gets more attention, since the symptoms are so obvious and extreme, with profound disruption of boundaries and self-regulation; but the depressive aspect of this is tied to the high, and can be very debilitating.

When the process involves the cyclic bipolar quality, the individual is challenged to see the entire cycle; when they go too high, they learn that a profound depression will likely follow; and when they are low, they can find the energy to begin to stabilize again. Often medication is helpful in finding the middle course to keep the individual's life on a more even keel; nevertheless an educational and relational approach such as we recommend can also be of great benefit. Some people find in relationship with others a sense of aliveness that may reduce their attachment to the high energy of manic episodes.

Personal Choices and the Neurochemistry of Depression

There is much controversy about the causes of depression. As we suggested above in our brief discussion of cyclical depressions, the most popular hypothesis at present is that depression is organically based. The assumption is that all moods and feelings are directly determined by neurology and neurochemistry. According to this view, some people inherit, through their genetic endowment, a makeup that is destined to express a depressive episode at some particular time in life. In its unnuanced form, this view is highly deterministic and mechanical. People who accept this position may abandon self-responsibility altogether, seeing their depression as an inevitable result of their genetic inheritance.

That the neurology and neurochemistry are important aspects of this problem cannot be denied; however, instead of seeing them as primary factors, we assume them to be secondary to the person's active (though mostly unconscious) choices in life. We believe that the genetic component provides a predilection towards certain choices; but the final common pathway is the self (the will and feelings) of the person. Thus, the organic factors may create a tendency towards depression; but it is individuals who create the circumstances in which such tendencies are expressed or not. In this view, a person's neurochemistry can often follow choice and behaviour, rather than necessarily determining it.

Personal choices and genetic predispositions are always in dynamic interplay. Although these two factors are interactive, the organic approach sees the self as secondary agent while we tend to see it as more primary. It is not a matter of either one or the other; to us, the important question is where in the process would it be most effective to intervene? Modern medicine offers drugs to shift the neurochemical balances that determine the moods of the individual. We recommend that people learn to face the issues around which they have become stuck or have made unhelpful life choices. Many depressed people who have taken this path have enjoyed a natural shift in their neurochemistry, evidenced by their movement out of the confines of their depressive straitjacket. Helping them to do so necessitates a broad understanding of the psychodynamics of depression. Often the use of antidepressant medications is a useful aid to assist people in the process; however, we have found that for many people it is not necessary to remain on these for long periods, once they have more understanding of their depressive process and are willing and able to engage responsively with it. We always advise people to address the issues of medication with their primary care medical practitioner, to arrive at an optimum approach for their particular situation.

16 **Energy Concepts and Health**

Metabolic Energy and Universal Energy

According to many energy theories, there are two types of energy: metabolic energy and universal energy. Metabolic energy is the byproduct of digestion and assimilation of food; it is a physical energy, which is limited and can be depleted. On the other hand, there is no limitation to universal energy; it is boundless, and ever present. In a broad view, these are the same: metabolic energy is a physical world expression of universal energy.

We have outlined in *Joining: The Relationship Garden* (Chapter 3) our view that most people have to some extent or another lost their sense of connection with universal energy. Consequently they must rely predominantly on metabolic energy to accomplish the things to which they aspire. This reliance entails certain beliefs about the nature of energy and can have sometimes dire consequences for our emotional, ethical, and physical health. In this chapter we look first at some of these beliefs and consequences, before returning to the possibilities that open up when one learns to reconnect with universal energy.

Energy Transfer:
A Common Misconception and Its Consequences

A commonly held belief is that a person can actually feel another's feeling. Indeed, this is sometimes proposed as a definition of empathy, much as understanding is defined as one's ability to know another's ideas. People talk about feeling another person's "vibes," suggesting some form of energy transfer; for example, people think they can feel someone else's anger or sadness by taking in the vibration. Many believe that one person can affect the lives of others through energy vibrations; in this way of thinking, people are seen to have responsibility for the emotional lives of those around them. A common notion is that some people's energy is "toxic" and should be avoided, while the energy of others is considered nutritive. Sometimes, "sensitive" people are thought especially liable to pick up this energy, to absorb it, to feel what others feel. This concept of energy tends to support the development of field dependence as we described it in Chapter 2, as well as a life style based on blame and victimhood. It is as though we are radio receivers in the midst of a huge number of transmitted energy vibrations, vulnerable to their influences.

This has some serious consequences for the way people approach relationships. Having lost touch with universal energy, many people depend almost solely upon their metabolic energy to maintain their relationships, through attempting to influence and control the people around them and their environment. Their lives are then characterized by obligations and roles, objectification and defensiveness. As we outlined in Chapters 2 and 3, these are features of a power-based, political approach to life rather than a strength-based, personal approach. Although this power-based approach can lead to great limitation in one's life, it is also an appealing option for many, providing excitement for some, and a sense of meaning or safety for others.

When people lose touch with universal energy, they commonly participate in a system in which people help each other and expect to be helped in return. They expend energy in taking care of each other's welfare and feelings. Indeed, this system has been institutionalized through social agencies whose purpose is to take care of other people. While these agencies clearly have their uses, they nevertheless tend to perpetuate the definition of some as clients or patients, and others as caregivers. In this model, people are ultimately seen as victims of one another and of circumstances, rather than as the creators of their own experience. This attitude can be very limiting to the growth and development of autonomous individuals. It is reflected in many of the essential concepts of therapy and healing. Patients tend to become entitled and irresponsible, and health care workers can "burn out" from trying to do the impossible, namely transmit energy to heal the people in their care.

An alternative view, which we espouse, is that people do not lose, expend or transmit energy. Rather they invest it. Sadly, they most often invest it in defense and protection, creating in themselves fixations and blockages. Their energy is not depleted; rather it becomes limited or stuck. If people can learn to let go of such blockages, they can re-mobilize their reserves of energy, and then need not be dependent upon others to help or heal them. In this same process they can also learn to reconnect with the potential of universal energy rather than relying so heavily on the resources of metabolic energy. In this way, people can move from a predominantly power-based approach to life towards an experience of their own strength in relationship with others and their environment.

Universal Energy and Resonance

Beyond the limitations of metabolic energy, we assume there is one universal energy that flows through all forms and beings. At human conception, that unity energy is particularized into the pattern of an individual, and enlivens that being during their entire life span. The body's metabolic processes are the means of utilizing that energy in each person; the energy is not created, it is organized. Fundamentally, the energy does not belong to the body; it belongs to the universe. We all swim in the same energy pool; thus, people always remain connected with one another at a deep energy level. The uniqueness of people is determined by genetically inherited traits that structure their energy patterns, in association with the energy blocks and resistances (Wilhelm Reich's "character armour") that they develop through experiences within their families and in society.[1]

Understood in this way, energy is in constant flow among all things and all people, blocked only by individual or group resistances. When people begin to loosen these resistances, they can experience what we refer to as resonance. Then, when a person hurts, others, who are always connected at a deep level, can feel their own hurt in resonance with the suffering individual. In similar fashion, when people understand someone else, they have a felt experience of understanding themselves as they resonate in relationship to the other. This is "recognition" (from the Latin *recognoscere*: to know again, and so to be reminded of something about the self connected to the other). In recognition, one person is stimulated to resonate and release static blocks to energy flow. To the extent that a person is free of the power motivation to take care of others, or to push others to change, or to escape the influence of others, that individual does not lose energy; instead, energy is set into motion within the individual as a resonance, which is experienced as a sense of aliveness, fullness, and movement. Instead of experiencing "burn-out," people in resonance feel more energetic and come to know themselves all the more. Because the energy is not their own, but rather is the expression of the infinite universal energy, it is always available. Thus energy is never lost, only restrained or liberated.

Reconnecting with universal energy and moving towards a strength-based approach to life is, then, a key to health on many levels. People are healthier physically, emotionally, and spiritually – and have healthier relationships – when their energy flows more freely.

Some Energy Concepts to Ponder

There are numerous energy approaches to health and healing. Shiatsu, rolfing, acupuncture, polarity therapy, Reichian body work, acupressure, and various forms of massage all utilize the concept of an underlying energy that can be released. Whether this energy is called *qi*, or *prana*, or vital force, or simply energy, the assumptions about it are similar. A common misconception is that energy is physical stuff, with physical properties; this is the process of reifying the energy (literally, making a "thing" of energy). We have found the following assumptions useful in moving beyond the restrictions of this mechanistic, physical concept of energy. As you read on, you may see that on one level energy is nothing but a series of concepts that can be useful in describing various phenomena. We think it is that, and more. It is also the miracle of life that emerges as one human soul is revealed to another; it underlies the ineffable, mysterious events that occur when two people meet and touch in intimate dialogue.

- *Energy is a life process, not a thing.* There is no such thing as energy; there is only activity that is described in terms of energy. So, when we speak of "life energy," this term describes activity, not a measurable physical entity. A person does not possess energy "stuff" that is bound up and needs release; rather, the individual expresses more personal potential by active engagement with the world.

- *Energy concepts describe invisible events.* The individual is involved in an active, dynamic process. In the Chinese articulation, energy is seen to be like the wind, which is invisible but has visible effects, such as the waves on top of a pond stirred by a breeze. The concept of energy is merely a useful way of describing the deeper, hidden patterns that are manifest in the individual personality.[2]

- *Energy is relationship in action.* According to Ida Rolf, the energy of the body exists in the relationship of the body structure to itself.[3] If the structures are bound together, the energy is fixated; if the structures have a more fluid relationship, the energy is less bound and hence more abundant in its effects. A variety of different energy conditions is possible at different times in an individual's life; the ancient Chinese concept of the five stages of change (which we describe in *The Illuminated Heart*) is an attempt to codify the categories within which the myriad energy states tend to organize. In this view, there is no good energy or bad energy; there are merely different conditions in which the individual's life process participates. It is not good to have high energy or bad to have low energy; "high energy" merely describes situations wherein the individual has much freedom of possibility and responsiveness, and "low energy" states involve retraction, and less differentiation of expression. When someone is radiantly alive, we speak of that person as freely expressing abundant life energy; conversely, an individual is said to be blocked in expression of energy in the states of illness or depression. If an individual is radiantly alive, this does not mean that the person has an abundance of some entity; if the person is depressed, it does not mean that some thing is lacking – rather, the energy is bound up in fixated patterns.

- *Energy is a process of change.* Life energy is a process in a continual flux. There are shifting alternatives of rest and movement, unfolding and folding, expansion and contraction, evolution and involution. All that remains constant is the process of change itself; even non-change is seen as a temporary state in the process of change.[4] This is the "forever flowing constancy" of Taoist philosophy.

- *Energy is an holistic concept.* The complaint of many people seeking attention for symptoms is that a mechanistic approach, which sees their symptoms as physically based, tends to ignore other dimensions of their being. Conceptualizing energy as a way to express the relationship between the various dimensions of the person can overcome the tendency to reduce the individual to an aggregate of symptoms. Von Bertalanffy puts it this way:[5]

  > We may state as a characteristic of modern science that the scheme of isolable units acting in one-way causality has proved to be insufficient. Hence, the appearances in all fields of science of notions like wholeness, holistic, organismic, gestalt, etc., which all signify that in the last resort, we must think in terms of systems of elements in mutual interaction.

- *Energy is unifying and integrating.* Energy can be seen to be the process of integration that unifies all dimensions of the individual – body, mind, spirit, emotions, and environment – into a whole person located in the cosmos. "Energy" is the relationship that exists between the various dimensions. The concept of energy can be useful in articulating the correspondence of one dimension with the others.

- *The energy body matrix might not exist.* In classical Chinese acupuncture theory, there is an energy body that underlies the other dimensions of being, radiating and giving rise to them. This energy body matrix is visualized as a circuitry of channels called meridians. Much scientific investigation has been devoted to the question of whether these meridians exist. Although the energy theory can explain some effects that have been experienced, no anatomical channels have been found, and no physical energy stuff has been isolated. But it does not really matter whether the energy exists and flows through meridians or not: this is at base a belief system, useful for organizing our perspective on reality. It is neither true nor false; it is merely a system of concepts. One does not have to prove that the energy exists in order to utilize the concept, any more than one has to believe that an actor on a stage is in fact the character represented in order to be moved by what is said. The process of utilizing any new belief system involves the willing suspension of disbelief – ceasing to resist long enough to see how the world looks when one assumes such a perspective.

- *Energy is relational.* In interaction with a client or friend one can appreciate the phenomenon of dialogue, where two energies meet. In this meeting, both individuals are challenged to become more present to themselves and each other; what occurs is the unfolding and expression of the potentials of each individual. Such a dialogue occurs on all dimensions – physical, emotional, intellectual, and spiritual. Integrative approaches to healing conceive of energy meetings at all the levels; thus, when one touches another person physically, many other, non-physical, interactions also take place. By utilizing non-limiting energy concepts, we make it possible to move beyond the perspective of the purely physical and become thoroughly relational.

For us, many of these concepts come together in our approach to the practice of acupuncture and our integration of classical Chinese medicine concepts into our work with people. If you have taken a Come Alive or other program at The Haven, you may have experienced a facilitator reading a person's Chinese pulses and applying needles or pressure to particular points on the person's body, as part of a relational process of personal exploration. Some years ago we wrote about our understanding of this process in an article called "The Needles are Not the Point,"[6] which we are now including in this book.

The Needles Are Not the Point

Most acupuncture theory is mechanistic, proposing that release of energy comes through insertion and manipulation of needles. Yet, the efficacy of treatment varies with different clients, and with different practitioners. Why is this? There is no widely accepted explanation for these variations. Usually, emphasis on practitioner training has been on better point location or more or less stimulation.

We propose that the client – not the practitioner or the needle – does the healing. This occurs when the client becomes open and vulnerable, responsive in energy to the self and the environment. When a person is open, the energy fixations that underlie disease states can release.

The personality is an expression of habituated conformations of the pattern of the energy body. Personal attitudes and habits can rigidify into chronic muscular and connective tissue tension – producing "blockages" in the energy, which manifest as illness. Illness is an expression of frozen energy, occurring when the energy body closes, or rigidifies. To heal, the person needs to thaw. The factors in the personality that encourage blockage are field dependency and roles and obligations, where the person is satisfying demands external to the self. A person opens up in intimate dialogue with self and others. Thus, the challenge is to help the client to establish intimate relationships with the self, and with others.

The release that permits the thaw can come through a variety of approaches. Acupuncture and moxibustion help to relieve blocks that permit freeing of the energy. In psychotherapy, clients can release pent-up psychological distress, with accompanying energy expression. Reichian breathing work involves unblocking of the energy fixations, with expression of feeling and relief from chronic tension. This can facilitate the opening of the energy body to encourage healing. We have found that deep breathing is very important to achieve maximum benefit from an acupuncture treatment.

Healing occurs in release of tension, with a reduction in fixation of energy. In a dynamic concept of energy, it is not the operation of the needle, but rather the life style of the client that facilitates healing. The relationship between client and practitioner is central to the healing process. The technique of the needle, or the application of electricity are not what make the release – it is the client himself or herself, in the relationship. Any operation at the points functions as a suggestion to which the client can respond. Indeed, one might conceivably sing to the points and help to facilitate release. The factors that the client offers in opening up the blocked energy are breathing, confidence in the relationship, and becoming personally responsible for self and life style.

In our work, we have moved to an educational model, where people can learn to discover themselves through open communication in a group setting. In this environment, acupuncture, breathing and other natural approaches are adjuncts to the life style change that underlies health. Holding back from other people through "walls" and roles is an expression of energy blockage, which can ultimately express itself in illnesses. Abandoning oneself to others, as occurs in compliant, dependent relationships ("fusion") results in confusion within the self which is often solved by control and defensive mechanisms that further freeze energy. Self-defining boundaries are necessary in maintaining full and healthy energy patterns. Much of our work involves facilitating communication, and developing skills for releasing the self through open, direct expression. All of our work is done in group setting now; the facilitation of communication is most thorough in this milieu. Sometimes there is an initial catharsis in the group process; the more substantial work for the individual involves adopting a life style of open and honest communication. The healing comes when people learn to resonate with themselves and each other.

People can learn to heal themselves by learning to release blocked energy through breath and clear interpersonal communication. Their ongoing dialogue with family and friends can establish a pattern of openness that facilitates high level wellness. In the process, people learn to have compassion for themselves and others in their deepening relatedness to life.

Part V

Issues and Opportunities

Each of us knows he is alive, and each of us seeks to be more alive, for each knows that far too often he is not as alive as he could be, as he really wants to be. Yet that is the way it is with us. Some days we are so alive, and some days we feel ourselves slipping under the death tide that is inexorably gathering within us. It is the great tragedy of the human experience that time and again we are blind and deaf to the opportunities for fuller living.

James Bugental[1]

17 Change and Transformation: The Risk of Becoming Yourself

To be what we are, and to become what we are capable of becoming, is the only end of life. – Robert Louis Stevenson[1]

Can a leopard change its spots, or a tiger lose its stripes? The human potential movement in North America was built on a foundation of hope for the overcoming of human shortcomings and woes. Since the proliferation of growth programs that began in the 1960s, many people have operated on the largely unexamined assumption that change is possible and that the potentialities of the human being are virtually limitless. This is frequently understood to mean that one does not have to tolerate personal or situational limitations: life is what you make of it, and you are totally responsible for everything that happens to you. If you don't like your life the way it is, you simply need to "get off your position" and create a new life more to your taste. In short, you are in the driver's seat, and the possibilities are limited only by your aspirations, your desire for change, and your willingness to "go for it."

The Morality of Change

The recipe for this way of living includes a liberal dose of moralism. People and events are seen in terms of right and wrong, or better and worse, or greater and lesser. In short, it's not okay today/here/now/with me-as-I-am; however, it could be okay tomorrow/there/then/with a better me. Life today is not so good; tomorrow might be better. I am not very realized today; I hope I will become something greater in the future.

This perspective has led people to a great deal of idealistic goal setting and personal ambition to change themselves or their circumstances. How often have you said or thought such things as "I need to change my life (work, partner)" or "When I finally accomplish this, then I'll be happier" or "When I finally achieve this, then everything will be great." The basic theme is that things are not okay as they are and that there is a better day coming in the future, after the necessary changes are made to create a richer life. Often, a deep-seated depression is at the root of this attitude (and is exacerbated by it), as people take the attitude that things are fundamentally unacceptable as they are. The ambitious drive to change oneself, one's life, or one's situation, in order to approach the desired changed condition, is pervasive. Many believe that with enough effort and attention, they can even restructure their personality, eradicating bothersome traits and giving birth to brand new ones. Generally, this thrust to change is accompanied by guilt and despair when aspirations are not realized.

Transcendence

Another interpretation of change involves a belief in transcendence, the notion that one can rise above one's circumstances and deal with it all from another plane. If life is bothersome, just ignore the troubling aspects and move beyond them. For those who adopt this frame of reference, there can be a floating feeling of blissful detachment. However, this approach operates against living participation, and people who adopt it are largely removed from the world and other humans. Hence, in transcending, people leave life without having fully entered it.

Devaluing the Self

The attempt to change oneself through idealism and striving into something better is generally accompanied by a continual self-devaluation. In all the years that we have worked with people, we have always found this attitude to be counterproductive to personal development. The more people try to get away from their situation, the more stuck and fixated they become. The mechanistic "change me" perspective and the idealism and hope of a better tomorrow operate against full participation in a life in the present. The goals of idealism kill present circumstances and interfere with the organic development of events. Craving for improvement interferes with the expansion of the present into a vigorous future. People become stuck in the attempt to escape from where they actually are. They are trying to affirm an image, a simulacrum of how things could be, and hence fail fully to exist. Thus, in existentialist terms, the pursuit of the illusion of change moves towards non-being.

We propose an alternative: to courageously resist the dissatisfaction of the achievement ethic, and affirm the substance of our lives in the present, thus contributing to the unfolding of beingness. Rather than focusing on an unreal image, we encourage people to face the facts of the living present, accepting their actual condition, and then proceed from here.

The Radical Hypothesis: Change and Transformation

As we have outlined in greater detail in *The Illuminated Heart*,[2] our hypothesis is this: at a fundamental level, change is not possible. One cannot change one's given biological structure or one's basic personality. Nor can you eradicate your life history by forcing yourself to ignore it.

Everybody is dealt a hand in life; most people are afraid to play their hand, or get mired in resentments over not receiving better cards. Wouldn't it be better to play out our hand as best we can, even with insufficient advice and information along the way?

We have found that this attitude frightens many. There is a certain security in getting ready for the future, which will be better. If one drops the pursuit of future betterment, and directly focuses on life as it is, a rush of fear floods in. Is this all there is? Is there no salvation from my lot? At least when I am sick, or in need of change, then I believe that I know who I am; I know what to expect of myself and others, and I have a certain sense of security in this. If I don't have this definition of myself as a patient, or as someone needing change, then who am I?

It seems likely that the structure of the personality is largely set from the early days of life. One inherits traits, and these are influenced by experiences in early childhood. By the time the individual is only months old, the basic personality pattern has been determined in quite a profound way. This deep structure, which is an amalgam of inherited tendencies, early experiences, and learning, will persist for the lifetime of the individual. The deep structure is not a thing, and it is not anatomically located; rather, it is formed of the interrelationships of deeply ingrained tendencies of activity in the personality. We assume that all so-called "therapies of change" that aim to alter the basic matrix of the personality are doomed to fail.

When people come to one of the programs we developed at The Haven with a certain "problem" they want "fixed" (that is, they want therapy), their initial work is to come to terms with their somewhat unrealistic ambition to get rid of this problem. If the identified problem is depression, they want to get rid of "it"; if they are allergic, they want a cure. If they have a tendency towards addiction (tobacco, alcohol, drugs, people), they want to have this addiction removed by some kind of psychological surgery. We recommend that they stop trying to get over the "problem," and instead sink into it and get to know it. As we suggest in Chapter 13, what people call allergies are often elaborate expressions of a deep fear of intimacy. Dependencies often mask an underlying issue of faith and commitment. "Depression" is often an umbrella term for the symptoms arising from emotional fixation and a withdrawal from contact and engagement.

In short, there does not need to be any problem at all! People are not diseases to be cured. Each is a unique human being, with a personal history, distinct tendencies, and idiosyncratic ways of experiencing life. If people relinquish their ambitious (and fruitless) desire to approach the "normal," they can more readily come to grips with who they actually are. Instead of therapies of change, we propose an educational uncovering and revelation, wherein each individual can become more aware. The key is to stop trying to get away from oneself and settle more deeply into one's own experience. Then something wondrous can occur; one can take charge of how to express oneself. This is the possibility of transformation.

Transformation

Although it is not possible to change one's history or deep structure, it is possible to transform the expression of the deep structure. The basic tendencies remain; how they are expressed can be modified. This transformation is quite different from a transcendence that springs from denial, where one tries to rise above oneself. In transformation, the basic deep structure is accepted, acknowledged, and studied. Ever-deepening self-knowledge arises from such an investigation of one's tendencies. In the absence of a struggle to change these patterns, one can become more and more aware of them, and even learn to anticipate them before they manifest themselves. Hence, it is possible to achieve a relative ease and freedom with oneself. The patterns are the basic plot of the play that one is living; if people know the lines and scenes, they can more fluidly perform their part. Like the pianist who is free to alter the expression and tones of a piece that is thoroughly practised and known, individuals have the opportunity to shift the emphasis between their various patterns (the "melodies"), once they know what these are.

Thus, transformation does not involve change of the deep structures; rather, it means shifts in perspectives on these patterns. The deep structures themselves remain the same; yet the expression is exquisitely varied and ever new. For example, the fascination with knives that many young children have (an early expression of a deeper structure) can be transformed into the grace and craft of the skilled surgeon. Or, the interest in incision and sharp cutting objects could also be transformed into the keen mental attitude of the discerning academic. As another example, the careful protection of the self from invasion by a foreign substance that typifies the allergic personality could well be used to design foolproof security systems. In short, there are creative outlets and uses for any personality pattern.

Foreground and background can shift. Take, for example, an individual who is outwardly defensive and difficult to approach, and inwardly very gentle and caring. This person could, with awareness, shift the emphasis of these two basic deep structures. The result could be a warm personality with strong self-definition.

Transcend and Include

In *A Brief History of Everything*, Ken Wilber outlined a concept of "transcend and include" which we find compatible with our notion of transformation. To Wilber, the basic structures do not change; however, their relevance and potency alter as the individual evolves. What is important to a child is often quite insignificant to the same person as an adult; nevertheless, the basic personality structure is the same, with a different emphasis. Wilber proposes that people should not try to rise above anything; as they proceed into the next developmental phase, they pass beyond the limiting constraints of fixed attitudes about their patterns, while retaining the essential features of the patterns themselves. Wilber says, "evolution is a process of transcend and include, transcend and include."[3] This is an example of holarchic, as opposed to hierarchic, thinking. In these terms, change is a feature of hierarchic thinking, where one state is considered higher or better than another; in transformation, on the other hand, one sees the whole and its component parts and invites the range of its possible expressions.

To us, evolution is a process of continuous transformation. People do not need to rise above their circumstances or change or get rid of parts of themselves. Rather, in relationship with others, they can repeatedly acknowledge and accept their patterns of existence, gaining deeper integration within themselves and making fresh choices about how they will express their patterns in the present.

When people adopt this attitude, they can see their existence as a landscape with different terrains and climates. No parts of the landscape need to be corrected or discarded. Indeed, their existence cannot be changed. But individuals do have the choice as to how much time they spend in the different parts of their landscapes, and how significant these parts are to them. This is the image we explored in Chapter 7.

Becoming More of Oneself

To summarize, then, it is our view that change of the basic personality is not possible. Often, seeking for change is a way of anaesthetizing the existential anxiety that accompanies life. To accept one's deep structures and tendencies often involves embracing this anxiety. To devote oneself to knowing one's basic patterns (and accepting the accompanying anxiety) rather than trying to eradicate them, will allow for more self-acceptance, more self-responsibility, and a greater inner strength.

Transformation is the ever-unfolding expression of deep knowledge of the self. The more thoroughly people know their patterns and tendencies, the more varied, creative, and spontaneous they can be. What others might call "change," we identify as transformation. In transforming, nothing new has been added. Individuals can only become more fully alive, more aware, more creative, more in touch with their place in relationship to others and to the universe as a whole. In short, all that people can become is more of themselves. Many people experience this as frightening and risky, yet the potential reward is a fuller experience of life, deeper relationships, and enhanced self-knowledge.

To Dare

To laugh is to risk appearing the fool.
To weep is to risk appearing sentimental.
To reach for another is to risk involvement.
To expose your ideas, your dreams,
before a crowd is to risk their loss.
To love is to risk not being loved in return.
To live is to risk dying.
To believe is to risk despair.
To try is to risk failure.
But risks must be taken, because the greatest hazard
in life is to risk nothing.
The people who risk nothing, do nothing,
have nothing, are nothing.
They may avoid suffering and sorrow,
but they cannot learn, feel, change,
grow, love, live.
Chained by their attitudes,
they are slaves;
They have forfeited their freedom.
Only a person who risks is free.

The pessimist complains about the wind;
The optimist expects it to change;
And the realist adjusts the sails.

— attributed to William Arthur Ward

18 Beyond Therapy: Discovery and Growth in Helping Relationships

The view of transformation which we proposed in Chapter 17 reflects a broadly structuralist approach to personal development and working with others, with a focus on patterns of behaviour and being. We contrasted this with a view of change that is more mechanical in nature, in which the emphasis is on trying to put right things about people that are thought to be broken or malfunctioning. This distinction echoes shifts in ways of thinking that Edgar Levenson, among others, outlined in the 1970s and 80s, the time when the two of us were beginning our collaboration together.

In his book *The Fallacy of Understanding: An Inquiry into the Changing Structure of Psychoanalysis*,[1] Levenson discussed three historical paradigms, which he saw expressed in society as a whole and in his own field of psychoanalysis in particular. He referred to these paradigms as mechanical, communications, and organismic or structural.

In this chapter we discuss these three paradigms as a way of helping readers understand the context in which we developed some of our views and ways of working with people; and also to encourage readers to consider how they think about their own lives, especially with regard to physical, emotional and spiritual illness, health and growth.

The Mechanistic Paradigm

Many of the advances of the early 20th century came about through an adherence to scientific thought and discipline. The human organism was seen as a miracle of mechanical perfection whose working parts could be isolated, studied, repaired when necessary, and even replaced when damaged or lost. In general medicine, this has remained the dominant paradigm ever since and out of it have come some remarkable techniques and treatments that have benefited people's overall health enormously.

Psychiatry at the beginning of the 20th century developed in this same paradigm through its close alliance with the medical model. Freud and his professional descendants were steeped in the mechanistic medical model; hence, modern psychology still contains within it a "psychohydraulic" notion about the psyche being like a machine. In mainstream medicine more attention has been given to the efficient working of the various physical parts than to the whole person. Similarly in psychiatry people have been seen as functioning inefficiently or inappropriately in society, or as somehow deviant from the norm.

Contained within this model is a hierarchical belief in authorities, who are deemed to know what is right or good for the specific patient and for people in general. In this paradigm, Levenson points out, the practitioner's goal is to facilitate insight into what is amiss within the person and what can be done to help. While this may have provided a sense of security for some, it has also spawned within patients a sense of helplessness about themselves and reliance on the physician-healer, of whom they stand in awe. Some people have this kind of relationship with their car mechanic; others probably know more about the workings of their car engine than they do about themselves!

The Communications Paradigm

Toward the end of the Second World War, a broad new understanding of communications developed; this was prompted by rapid advances in electronic technology, many of which had been developed for the purposes of war. The onset of the communications era was rapid and dramatic, reaching its peak in the 1960s, when its offspring were old enough to exert power and influence over the direction of society's systems. Amidst the social and political disorder of the times there arose some new visions of people and their place. Problems of all sorts were seen to be issues of communication and information transfer. Professionals in the behavioural sciences developed a great interest in trying to enhance communication between people; this gave rise to theories of social psychology and studies in communications.

This was a generation of immediate gratification (sometimes labeled a culture of narcissism) with "here-and-now" interest in the present, a rapid identification with groups (minority, majority, special interest, and so on) and a valuing of change, often merely for the sake of change. The prevailing fear of the individual was fear of isolation; people had to "belong." These factors had an influence on the helping professions of the day.

Amidst this interest in communication, humanistic psychology rose to the fore, championed by growth centres such as Esalen Institute in California, and popularized by the media. Humanistic practitioners, dissatisfied with traditional psychotherapy – which appeared to be time-consuming, expensive and of limited availability to the public, and apparently often unsuccessful – developed a wide spectrum of methods, some new, many ancient. Thus, a whole array of techniques and vocabulary was developed outside the auspices of traditional psychology and medicine; these included gestalt therapy, rolfing, encounter groups, T-groups, psychodrama, art and drama therapy, dance and movement therapy, meditation, Reichian breathing, primal therapy, and transactional analysis. We ourselves were part of this transformative time, and we embraced humanistic ideas, incorporating them into our work with people, and developing out of them the models which have now been taught for decades at The Haven. Many of the techniques characteristic of this paradigm have now been assimilated into institutional programs and educational centres.

A practitioner working in the communications mode will be attentive not just to the content of a client's story (note the shift in terminology from patient, as used in the mechanistic paradigm, to client), but also to the quality of the presentation, alert for clues that help to fill in the full meanings that the person is trying to convey, often unconsciously. The practitioner acts as a good listener, attempting to understand and to help the client to come to that understanding. When this is effective, the client experiences being understood, and hence no longer isolated. A therapeutic session in this mode functions in much the same way as a confessional; people overcome the barriers that create isolation by contacting another human being, in this case their practitioner, and revealing themselves. When the failure to communicate is overcome, it is thought, the illness is no longer necessary.

In the mechanistic paradigm we described above, illness was seen as a kind of malfunctioning of parts; what was needed was insight to identify the problem (diagnosis) and then action to correct it (drugs, diet, or surgery, for example). In this view, illness is accidental, or a result of helplessness or aging, a failure of will, or a consequence of victimization by external circumstances. From the perspective of the communications approach, on the other hand, illness represents an attempt to communicate. What is needed is not insight, but understanding. People presenting with symptoms are attempting to "say" something about their experience of the world that they seem unable to express in any other way. Thus, there is contained within any illness, psychological or physical, a story from that person's life.

Often clients are unaware of the messages they are trying to convey through their illnesses; indeed, it is generally this lack of understanding of what they are trying to communicate that results in the production of symptoms. Illness sometimes manifests when a person doesn't know how to communicate in any other way. An example of this might be the angry eruptions in psoriasis, which may manifest in face of a person's inability to express anger more directly. Implicit in this concept is the notion that if people could find other ways to communicate, they would not have to be sick. People who are manifesting illness often experience being isolated and believe that they are not understood; indeed, they likely are not understanding themselves. You will see elements of this approach in our accounts of working with people with phobias, allergies, and MS in Chapters 13 and 14.

One difficulty with the communication approach is that, although the symptoms are often alleviated in the short term, lasting change may not occur. Clients who experience being understood, and thus less isolated in contact with the listening professional, often return after the appointment to the same life style, and continue to live in ways that maintained the illness pattern in the first place. As we outlined in Chapter 17, we believe that lasting change rarely occurs without individuals becoming aware of the contextual patterns in which they live, and then taking responsible actions to deal with the patterns they uncover. This perspective is characteristic of the structuralist or organismic paradigm which began to emerge in the last three decades of the 20th century.

The Structuralist Paradigm

As Levenson was writing in the 1970s, the sociocultural landscape was undergoing a major shift. Led by environmentalists who were becoming increasingly aware of the threat that humanity was posing to itself, other species and the environment, and with a perspective that emerged from seeing the first photographs of the earth from outer space, a whole new wave of awareness swept the Western world. A natural philosophy of interdependence began to be voiced by sociologists and anthropologists, who started to outline an order in the universe based upon interrelated systems. This structuralist philosophy (studying the predilection towards "structuring" into certain patterns) gradually began to pervade all walks of life. The health practitioners who embraced it became interested in their clients' patterns of individual behaviour (their life-styles); they attempted to clarify these patterns for people, so that individuals could have more awareness of their responsibility and how their actions affected both themselves and others. Their focus was on the consequences of behaviour, freedom of choice with sensitivity to others, and valuing of individuality and idiosyncrasies within a social and global context.

In the structuralist approach, therefore, clients are seen within a larger context of interconnected relationships, but are nevertheless full, active agents in their own lives. They are not victims of outside forces; rather, when they are ill, they are viewed as living in such a way as to participate in illness. Illness persists because of the lack of awareness of the patterns that produce it. When clients become aware of these patterns, they can alter or avoid them. As we have said before, this self-responsibility, which includes being responsible for the illness patterns, is different from blame. People are responsible for having a cold, or a broken arm, insofar as they are participating in the illness process or the events leading to an accident. However, the person with the illness is not to blame – no one is. This is not a moral situation. Rather, from the structuralist viewpoint, what is significant is the awareness of process, and coming to appreciate one's relationship to that process. With adequate awareness, people can shift their relationship to the illness process.

Thus, as Levenson wrote, in the structuralist paradigm "we are no longer as interested in the machinery, as we are in its patterns of consequence."[2] If insight is the primary goal in the mechanical paradigm, and understanding the goal in the communications paradigm, then awareness is the goal of the structuralist paradigm.

Practitioners functioning in this framework adopt a phenomenological approach. Their aim is, as fully as possible, to come to see and appreciate the world through the client's eyes. Thus, they value empathy and inclusion. These practitioners will not try to manipulate their clients' lives from arm's length (this would reflect a mechanistic approach) or passively listen and understand (the communication paradigm); instead, they become involved in their clients' experiences, mutually sharing thoughts, interpretations, and feelings as a way of facilitating clients' awareness of themselves in relationship to their practitioners, and ultimately to their families, society, and the world.

Vital to this process, Levenson points out, is the practitioner's ability "to be trapped, immersed and participating in the client's system, *and then to work his way out*" (the italics are ours).[3] To do this requires an awareness that both client and practitioner function by attempting to draw other people and events into their own story, their own perspective on the world. This is how we make sense of things, and how we limit ourselves. If the practitioner can understand the client's perspective without being "sucked in" to their story and losing their own perspective – if, in Levenson's phrase they can resist being transformed by the other – then they will be practicing the art of inclusion, as we have described it in *The Illuminated Heart* and elsewhere. Inclusion is "an existential turning of one's existence to the other and the attempt to experience that person's side as well as yours." It requires a "back-and-forth movement of being able to go over to the 'other side' and yet remain centred in one's own existence."[4]

Being met in this way by another can help the client himself become aware of the limiting perspectives in which he traps himself; it is as if for a moment he puts aside his blinders and opens himself to a wider field of vision. It is in this way that a person can adjust his relationship to his patterning, his deep structure and its many isomorphic expressions; this is what we described in Chapter 17 not as change but as transformation.

In this way, the function of the helping relationship is fundamentally to help people discover a broader viewpoint. "The larger and wider the patient's perspective," wrote Levenson, "the better equipped he is to live in the real world."[5]

As we have seen, this challenges practitioners to bring themselves as persons to the encounter. The challenge for the client, on the other hand, is to take the awareness gained in the helping encounter into regular life. We agree with Levenson that the way to do this is to develop a life of dialogue and intimacy. As he put it:[6]

> I would prefer that patients leave therapy committed to the lifetime pursuit
> of dialogue, with the recognition that "intimacy" may be more the epiphany
> of hard work at living than the directed goal.

As Levenson points out, it was practitioners of family therapy and group therapy who found the transition from a communications paradigm to a structural model most natural.[7] The interrelatedness of social systems was presumably more apparent in these contexts than in the traditional one-on-one therapeutic encounter. In our own collaboration together, we worked with groups from very early on, seeing in them enormous potential for people to "knock up against" perspectives different from their own, to engage dialogically with others, and to use these awarenesses to adjust their own perspectives. Our groups were made up of people of a wide range of ages and backgrounds, and indeed our colleagues have extended this to include children and teens in programs at The Haven.[8]

In this way, we moved away from an essentially therapeutic model (whether mechanical or communications based) towards one that we count as educational, wherein we invite people to become aware of their own patterns of thought and behaviour and to make for themselves the sometimes difficult decisions about what they will do with their lives.

An Educational Approach

We make a basic distinction between therapeutic models and educational models. Therapeutic models work from a basic understanding that people are in some way "broken" or functioning inefficiently or inappropriately. The educational model we espouse is different. The root of the word "education" is a Latin word meaning to "lead out from." Thus, for us, education involves drawing out what is already there as potential. The structuralist view we have described in this chapter assumes the individual to have pre-existing patterns at all levels of being. Structuralist education provides the stimulus to awaken inherent potentials within individuals, helping them to discover personal truths within themselves. In this holistic approach, people are seen to be complete within themselves; initially they are inexperienced and unexpressed, more potential than actualized, but they are not broken or incomplete. The task of education is to facilitate people's discovery and expression of themselves, their own nature, and their place in the world. The mirroring and stimulation of interpersonal relationships provide tools for people to grow to fruition. We call this form of education "heuristic," that, is concerned with discovery. The term comes from the same Greek verb that gives us "Eureka," meaning "I have found it."

To educators of this persuasion, the challenge is to create situations in which people are able to discover their own possibilities. When this model is applied to the helping and healing professions, clients are not seen as illnesses that need to be cured, but rather as beings who have the capacity to discover themselves in an educational process. Traditional therapy and conventional education often undermine self-development; structuralist education aims to bring forth the realized person, full of promise and challenge and bounty. Teachers and health practitioners can be seen as midwives, helping people to give birth to themselves, to actualize the potentials that their deep structure holds as a promise. The method is applied in intimate dialogue person-to-person, rather than in the power dynamics of conformity and "fixing." As such, it is not limited to professional relationships between practitioners and clients but can be explored in groups, families and in relationships between individuals who are willing to engage with one another with honesty and curiosity.

To quote Levenson, such an approach offers, in all these contexts:

> not cure, peace of mind, idealized relationships, but awareness, the exhilaration of reality, of the sense of struggle, and the opportunity of being flooded with the variety, richness and unending flux of human experience.[9]

This is what we have sought for ourselves and in our work with others at The Haven and around the world.

19 From Survival to Discovery: Options in the Wake of Abuse

We first published the material contained in this and the following chapter nearly 20 years ago, when the subject area was a "hot topic" in many circles. In the intervening period, some of the ideas we put forward have perhaps become more commonly held, and the helping professions may have moved their focus elsewhere. And yet, abuse is at least as common as it was then, and the dangers for counsellors and their clients that we identified 20 years ago remain pertinent today. Indeed, we think the principles we outline in these chapters are vitally important for people who have experienced abuse, or who have memories of abuse, and for their counsellors and friends.

Working with people over many years, we have heard and encountered many horrifying stories of childhood trauma, including the blind outbursts of alcoholic parents, the pain of neglect, and the ravages of early child sexual abuse. We have also worked closely with a number of individuals whose unfolding memories reveal episodes of repetitive ritualistic assaults. The degree of objectification of young lives invites outrage, horror and pain on the part of the attending professional. We ourselves have been shocked to discover the extent of this objectification that has occurred for so many people. Often, these people have tried to forget, to bury their previous pains with patterns of coping and withdrawal; they are often plagued by fears and myriad psychophysiological symptoms. It is in this state of current distress and disability that they seek the help of professional counsellors and other helpers.

Caring Is Not Enough

Professionals can help to uncover early memories, and to provide safe nutritive environments where people can update themselves, and learn to trust and to care in open and sharing atmospheres in the present. Counsellors can help people to revisit old wounds, so that they can express their pain and outrage in the present, in order to unlock the restrictions in themselves, mentally, physically, emotionally and spiritually. These people do need a caring, supportive environment in which they can face their lives, put their history into perspective, and practise using underdeveloped wills. But caring is not enough!

The problem has now been recognized; agencies have been established to help, and programs to provide rehabilitation. Social services are now involved with prevention, by working with young people who are in need. Professionals can often recognize the signs of child abuse, and can sometimes take action to ease a child's pain. Generally, these solutions are legal and political. Laws are passed, which society endeavours to enforce. There are concerted efforts to ferret out perpetrators, to rectify wrongdoing. However, there is another insidious aspect, which helpers, agencies and clients are not facing squarely.

The Concept of "Survivor"

It has become fashionable to talk of the "wounded child." As counsellors help people to reclaim earlier memories, and to express previously repressed pains, these clients then are prone to explain all of their current circumstances as being caused by their earlier abuses. Others feel pity for them, and want to try to rectify past wrongs with current caregiving. Some become their champions and want to be their saviours. Unfortunately, in the attempt to provide help and services, caregivers tend to become involved in fixating people as victims.

For many, it has become a way of life to be a "survivor" and an "adult child of... (fill in the blank: for example, adult child of alcoholic parents, etc.)." Guilt-ridden agencies and institutions provide much support for this stance, and many well-intentioned counsellors are contributing to keep clients fixated as helpless nonparticipants in earlier life activities. For some, early abuse is an icon to be worshipped, a talisman to wear proudly, as a testimonial to endurance and fortitude. Unfortunately, for some people, it is used as a justification for complaining, a reason to wallow in past pains rather than face life in the present. Although we believe one can find self-respect in expressing indignation and outrage, the self is diminished by blame and faultfinding. As long as people use their past traumas and abuse to justify and account for their current lifestyle and circumstances, they are ignoring the importance of their own will. They can use this as an excuse not to develop themselves, and not to learn and grow in their current relationships. Often their counsellors are in effect conspiring with them, to keep them fixated as victims.

The concepts of the "wounded child," the "child within," and other similar notions have been useful in giving language to feelings and memories that are sometimes difficult to access. However, as with most concepts that begin as fresh innovations, these ideas are now becoming trite and overused. Often, adults who have been abused become like spoiled children in their bid for attention. Strangely, these people who have often had so little, become entitled and demanding. They want to be attended to, fixed, heard, and pitied. Their attitude becomes "give me what I want to make up for what I missed," or "I have been wronged, or damaged, and I need taking care of," or "I am incomplete, and need help." Thus, these people fail to individuate. In a way, they fail to take ownership of their past. Instead, their past is seen as something that "happened" to them.

The Task of the Professional

The task of the professional is to provide a safe atmosphere in which these individuals can uncover their past hurts and pain, and investigate them in the light of their current lives. Generally, these people have not learned to relate in consistent boundaried ways. They did not have the circumstances to learn to say "no," or to use their will to determine what they wanted. They often have shrunk back from life, tightened up in fear and denial, and are living restricted lives. These people can learn to take ownership of their feelings from the past, and move on into fuller lives.

Working with victims involves sequential facilitation. At the beginning, the person needs support and help to uncover repressed material and feelings. This early "dependency phase" can help make up for early childhood experiences that were missed. Then when the person has found more personal strength, and has experienced dependability in interacting with another, he or she can develop more mature relationships in the present. Often, the counsellor is the first person with whom the client has dared form a close relationship. Once a strong bonding is made with the counsellor, the next step in the project is for the person to extend newly found interactive skills into relationships with peers.

Stages in Working Through Past Trauma

We believe four stages are possible in working through past trauma.

- *Stage 1. Awareness:* The client is helped to recognize past experience, to uncover earlier memories and to acknowledge them.

- *Stage 2. Affect Expression:* The client is helped to express the pent-up pain and anger, to go through these emotions, rather than bury them (as they probably have done to this point). This should not be only verbally; instead, we encourage an energetic body approach, to unlock the energy that is stuck in the body. At first, this expression will likely be heavily laden with blame. As the work progresses, the client can become more involved in self-affirmative expression of feeling without so much blame. In this way, the person begins to shift from blame to responsibility for his or her own feelings.

- *Stage 3. Sharing:* Clients share their feelings and experience with others – with individuals, or in safe group settings. By relating their experiences to others, they can reduce the charge of secrecy, and begin to see their lives in a broader context. By others' empathetic witnessing, people can learn to see that they are not alone in the present. The person can have time-limited comfort, and then be encouraged to engage in life. This is a fine line. People certainly need to experience compassion, caring and empathy; however, they must also move through and beyond dependency upon the attention of others to discover their own curiosity for life, and their own empathy for others.

- *Stage 4. Discovery:* The person can now begin to discover life without the victim stance, and to develop responsible relationships.

One Woman's Story

A 37-year-old woman, who had endured early abuse and sexual violence, described her uncovering of memories in counselling as follows:

Remembering all these experiences really shook up my world. It explained many of the struggles I've had in my life, especially regarding my sexuality. It also changed the way I saw myself. I began to see myself as a victim of sexual abuse – small, powerless, helpless, bound. I didn't like the word "victim" so I thought of myself as "wounded" instead. And since I had been wounded, I needed to be healed.

Her counselling proceeded:

I spent the next three years seeking to be healed of the effects of being sexually abused. I faithfully saw a counsellor, attended workshops and a support group, prayed, made retreats, journalled, drew and read books. I found all these things helpful and I could see progress, but I never seemed to attain that elusive goal of being healed. Since I was not yet healed I felt unable to make decisions about my life. I put my life on hold waiting to be healed.

She waited for healing from outside of herself:

I realize now that in seeing myself as a victim I believed that my healing was out of my control. Since I'd been abused by someone else I needed to be healed by someone else. At first I thought that my counsellor would be the one to heal me. When I realized that this wouldn't happen, I decided that it was God who would somehow heal me. I tried hard to do my part and carried on faithfully with my process while waiting for God to do His part. Yet this never seemed to happen and I began to despair that I would ever be healed. I had become stuck on a merry-go-round of feeling victimized and powerless, waiting for something or someone to magically heal me, and feeling even more victimized and powerless when that didn't happen. I became frustrated, exhausted and stuck, unable to get on with my life.

She then attended a residential personal development seminar at The Haven:

I came to the group looking for someone or something to heal me. My turning point came one day when the leaders explained how we live in the future instead of the present when we live in hope. I realized with surprise that I was living in hope for the day I would be healed and could get on with my life. I decided I could let go of the idea of being healed, and live my life as it is today. I shared this with one of the leaders, and he said, "Yes, and you don't even have to think of yourself as injured!" I suddenly understood! I'd never thought of myself as injured before all this – why did I think of myself as injured now? I'm the same person I was before I started remembering all this stuff! At that moment I stopped believing I was an injured victim waiting to be healed. I began to see myself once again as an intelligent, caring and competent woman. I know that I have experienced sexual and physical abuse, but I no longer see myself as powerless or helpless. Rather, I believe that I have developed a lot of inner strength as a result of my experiences. I feel freer and once again able to make decisions about my life. And now I can make these decisions much more fully than I ever could before.

She was amazed to discover:

I'm not injured or flawed... I'm whole.

She had thought her life was doomed because of her early experiences, rather than to see that she was now an adult who could make different choices with more authority than when she was young. She said,

I have been afraid of men, but now as an adult, I can make choices not to simply avoid men.

Common Misconceptions

Too often, counsellors leap to the conclusion that any current trouble is the expression of past abuse. Indeed, some people endured much violation; however, there does not seem to be a clear correlation between degree of abuse and degree of current difficulty. There is a danger of the therapeutic endeavour becoming a parody where everything in the present is explained by past traumas. Without denying the seriousness of early abuse, professionals must not make the mistake of trying to witch-hunt every vestige of the past. Not all current problems can be explained by early abuse.

Not everyone who has a memory was abused. We know of a young man who explained his delayed adolescent rebellion with his parents by his assertion that he was sexually abused by his parents as a child. His only evidence was a vague memory, which we believe was constructed after a well-intentioned therapist suggested it to him. The old dictum, "Follow your clients, don't lead them," is crucial. Helpers should not put more ideas of abuse into people's minds.

Fixation on "Abuse": A Second Story

Sometimes counsellors become so fixated on "abuse" that they miss hearing what a client is trying to tell them. Another woman we met had sought help from a counsellor for a depression following the untimely death of a close friend. These are her words:

> At age 51, this was my first psychotherapeutic experience. I had no idea what to expect, no frame of reference with which to evaluate the quality of the therapy other than an acquaintance referral plus my blind faith in the counsellor's friendliness, to which I immediately was attracted. Friends seldom mentioned therapy except as an adjunct to their failing marriages or their kids' brushes with drugs or delinquency. With a healthy marriage of 30 years and four "good" kids, I had remained a counselling virgin who had managed life to that point with no knowledge of the risks or benefits of therapy.

She began to experience improvement.

> Weekly sessions at $80 per hour commenced with my commitment to attend three sessions. My depression improved immediately, just from the counsellor's warmth and empathy. Then I agreed to stay on in therapy to address other life improvements. Since insurance was not reimbursing this therapy, there were no external checks or time limits. Five years and more than $20,000 later, we were still locked in a therapeutic alliance.

In the course of her therapy, she disclosed an early experience to her therapist:

What seemed to cement my need for long term therapy was my disclosure toward the end of our fifth session that I had been incested by my father from age 2½ to 11½. Sucking in her breath, my counsellor had grabbed my knee as if to capture a "live one" before it got away. I was surprised by her zeal to explore this issue that I had relegated to the dustbin of past history, not knowing that this was a hot issue in the world of psychotherapy.

She describes her ongoing efforts to discover her anger over the past incidents:

Attempting to access my anger over nine years of incest was sine qua non on my counsellor's agenda from then on. Any positive feelings I shared about my father's enjoyment of my body, the nurture I had experienced in his warmth and cuddling, fell on deaf ears or were contradicted. My father was labelled a criminal who had "abused, molested and betrayed" his daughter. I remember those words exactly, because I carried them on a flash card in my purse for several months. I found these indictments hard to swallow because they invalidated my feelings, distorted my reality. Instead of anger at my father, I became furious at my counsellor.

My confusion was compounded when I attended several agency-facilitated survivor groups over the next few years. In each case, the main agenda was to access rage over the all-inclusive, heinous crime of child sexual abuse. In many cases, I judged that a survivor's anger was justified. I shared buckets of tears with them over beatings, burnings, bondage and other hurtfully inflicted perversions; but I felt like a white elephant when expected to kick and scream on my own behalf against my incestor. He had acted tender and loving with me. I had for the most part enjoyed being cherished, being aroused sexually, being penetrated by his penis, being enveloped by his warmth. My healing could not be predicated on accessing an anger I did not feel.

The counselling continued:

Private weekly counselling continued with the same therapist, to whom I was now inextricably bonded. In an attempt to please her, I kept trying to feel anger toward the incest so my counsellor could "wash me clean" and we could get on with other issues, now stacking up like cord wood. Compulsive eating, yo-yo dieting with a loss and regaining of over 100 pounds,

low self-esteem, neurotic behaviour patterns, emptying nest, uterine can-
cer followed by a radical hysterectomy, instant menopause, resumption of
smoking and drinking, sudden onset of asthma and arthritis, fibromyalgia,
strabismus, spiritual crisis, career change – nothing could get my counsel-
lor's attention like the incest/anger issue. We locked ourselves in stalemates
for months at a time, always with her implication that once the anger was
released, other issues would fall into place. Where, oh where was my anger?

She remained dependent upon her counsellor.

After our fourth year together, my counsellor periodically broached the
subject of termination. Each time, I would panic. How could we abandon
each other when I still had not found my anger? What about all those other
unprocessed issues? Was I to flunk counselling as I had almost flunked
college statistics, because I was missing a point? Childhood memories were
triggered about feeling abandoned by my absentee mother, and the num-
erous housekeepers who filled in for her. I felt like I would die without my
counsellor's support. I wanted to be her friend forever, or be locked in ther-
apy with her for the rest of my life. We terminated three months ago. Her
door closed forever on future contacts except for once a year tune-ups. I still
often feel bereft, and silently grieve the loss of that significant relationship.

After leaving counselling, she attended a residential personal development seminar at The Haven. In a session, the simple question "Is it possible
that you enjoyed your sexual relationship with your father, and that you
don't have anger about it?" brought a shocked look, and a sudden outpour-
ing of relief from the woman. She concludes her report with the following
passage:

As of this writing, I am attending a two month program at The Haven. A
new way to look at the issue of child sexual abuse has been suggested for me
to consider, one that seems to be more in line with my own sense of reality.
"Who told you that you had to get angry when you're not?" asked one of the
directors. Am I being heard at last? Are my feelings being validated? Am I
now free to invest energy in new directions of personal growth?

Moving Beyond Objectification

Both offenders and victims need to move beyond the objectification of
the "bad" perpetrator and the "wounded" victim. Both are human beings
contending with boundary issues and fixations of energy. Generally, the
perpetrators of violence or abuse become objectified as the "bad one," the

"offender," the "guilty one." This objectification does nothing to help either the perpetrator or the victim. Perpetrators have objectified their victims; then the victims remain stuck in objectifying the offenders. In one of our programs, we had a very intense and dramatic encounter between a young woman and an older man; she was a previous subject of childhood violence, and he was the person who had actually committed the offenses against her. As she faced him with her rage and pain, exploding with pent-up frustration and vehemence, she asked him "How could you have done this?" The perpetrator, suddenly faced with the real life feelings of the person rather than his objectified victim, broke down crying with remorse and impotence. He wept to see her pain, and was suddenly shocked loose from the impersonal world of objects into a human dialogue. If the young woman had remained stuck in just punishing him, she would have remained fixated in litigious revenge. As she cleared her feelings, she began to develop a genuine curiosity about him. He was stimulated to look into himself, and cried openly about his own childhood trauma. Suddenly, both people were looking beyond their own entitled fixations on power and revenge, and were seeing the humanness of each other. This young woman has gone on to develop a meaningful relationship; the perpetrator continued to seek help to uncover the sources of his own poor boundaries. Both people in this abuse situation, victim and perpetrator alike, were contending with inadequate boundaries, and limited personality development.

The Challenge for Counsellors, Friends, and Family

Health professionals, as well as friends and family, often lack the self-awareness and tools to help people work through the issues we have been discussing. They are commonly afraid of their own pain, and try to relieve pain in others, rather than experience their own in response to others. Often, they might be willing to help, but don't know what to do. Although counsellors are generally well-intentioned, they are prone to collaborate in keeping these people dependent and fixated on their pasts. It is tempting to contribute to a prolonged dependency because of a need to be important to someone else. Rather than encourage gradual development in the present, counsellors sometimes keep these people weak and dependent to serve their own inadequacies (without realizing that this is occurring). Often, helpers are arrested at the same level as their clients, and gain false power by taking care of them, rather than facing their own fears and insecurities. Many times, counsellors have themselves experienced similar traumas to their clients, and are prone to fuel the clients' distress with their own. Instead of participating in mutual pity, professionals should be encouraging their clients to live in the present, and put the past into its place – as a memory. These comments apply also to the friends and family of people who have experienced abuse.

Counsellors Who Have Experienced Abuse

Counsellors who have had early trauma can be an inspiration, if they have worked through the situation. Often, the client can benefit from relating to someone whose life is working well, who can say, "I made it out... so can you." We have worked with a young woman who was a victim of a satanic cult, raised from infancy in horrid rituals to be a high priestess. At this point in her life, she has no regrets for her past, even though she has come through several life-threatening illnesses that were associated with buried memories.[1] She is now a counsellor, and she says,

> I can resonate with people who have experienced pain like me, and have compassion for them. My training as a counsellor has come from my living through the pain of my earlier life. Now, in a strange way, I'm glad I have this experience, although I wouldn't wish it on anyone else.

As she continues in her personal development process, she writes:

> I am also very aware now that I have maintained a "victim's" position throughout a great deal of my life. I have had trouble acknowledging that I often feel victimized, but my language and my stance in difficult situations has brought this information to my awareness. I had always thought of myself as someone who was tough, but now I see that even though I toughed my way through a lot of things I often did not acknowledge the fear or the hurt and it has built up over time. I think through using the communication model and noticing the number of times I say "she did that" or "you make me," I have finally realized that on a deep level I take a position of being the victim to my life. That is changing. I laugh now at how I slip so easily into blame. My partner is also a constant reminder, always commenting when I say something using language that implies I have no control or responsibility.

She has much insight to share:

> Since being ill I have had to look at almost all the areas in my life that I avoided – my sexuality, my relationship to my family, my style of communication, my sadness, my incredible neediness and desire to remain

helpless. At times I have been repulsed, scared, ready to quit. I believe the journey has taken a tremendous amount of courage and the outcome has not been glory or sympathy but simply life. I think I wanted to get even on some deep level, to draw attention to myself, to not have to become interested in anyone else, and to be able to avoid caring. Instead I have learned about loving. I still sometimes want more than that. But I know that comes from a place of fear. Life is not about glory or honour or right and wrong; those paths have led me to death. Life seems to be more unpredictable and has little to do with fairness.

Discovering Life

Counsellors or friends cannot make up for someone else's past; nor can they undo it. They can hurt and rage with them, and help them to discover appropriate forms of expression in their current lives. People can be curious not so much about "How were you abused?" but rather, "What did you experience?" The former question involves a stuckness in moral strictures; the latter acknowledges the individual's own experience, which often involves ambiguities of pleasure and coexisting pain. If some of the acts were pleasurable, the person might have repressed guilt feelings, which can be expressed in a variety of ways.

When individuals discover that they have been abused, this revelation does not provide the answers for the rest of their lives. Even when people have horrible things to work through, there comes a time when they must let them go, and move on. This is not to excuse the inhuman violences of the past, nor to deny the importance of the political and legal efforts in this area. However, professionals must go beyond political and legal solutions, into personal sharing with the people who are in danger of becoming lost or fixated in the concept of themselves as wounded children. James Hillman describes the importance of listening deeply to people, instead of quickly labelling them:

Whenever treatment directly neglects the experience as such and hastens to reduce or overcome it, something is being done against the soul. [2]

The goal is for people to understand themselves, but not to rationalize current shortcomings. Thus, no one should excuse people's behaviour in the present because of past memories. The task for everyone is to learn to use their will to have maturing interpersonal relationships, and to develop a growing sense of responsibility for themselves. Whether it comes from counsellors, colleagues or friends, empathetic understanding offers much more than does pity and caretaking. The traumas of past experiences need to be honoured, but not venerated. Dealing with the pain and suffering from the past can be a way of discovering life; but, this should not become a way of life!

20 Memories of Abuse: A Call for a Balanced Perspective

Memories are to the mind what feelings are to the heart. In their own way they both provide texture to our lives. – Bennet Wong

We opened the previous chapter with the observation that when we first wrote about sexual and physical abuse, the issue was a "hot topic" in society at large and in the helping professions. It became apparent to us at the time that attitudes to memory were an important part of the ongoing discussion and greatly affected the experience in the present of people who were being seen by ourselves, and by other counsellors. In this chapter, we argue for a balanced perspective on the importance and reliability of memories, and caution against a tendency to become "fixated" in one's pursuit of the past.

Fixation on Memories

Human beings have a remarkable proclivity to become fixated, to become repetitious and addicted in attitudes and activities. People seem to abhor newness, and want to set things into a familiar pattern. Most people become fixated in order to find something dependable, as a way of alleviating ontological anxiety (see Chapter 6).

It is often suggested that an important way of "getting to know oneself" is to look into one's past, and find explanations for current circumstances from recollections of early childhood experiences. In our opinion, investigating oneself and one's past life can be useful, for a period of time, and for perspective. However, there is a very great danger that a person can become addicted to this procedure, and become more interested in indulging in the memories than in living in the present; the person becomes self-stimulated by more and more memory unfolding – a sort of experiential masturbation. The memories supersede lived reality. We think that a few visits to one's traumatic past should be enough; any more verges on indulgence and sentimentalism. One can become fixated upon self-investigation, becoming a "memory junkie." This is the same as with the process of any addiction; the addiction becomes more important than contact. To the alcoholic, the drink supersedes contact and relationship with the world and people around. The current fashion of focusing on remembering provides a dangerous situation, wherein the individual can indeed become addicted to the memory seeking, and lose perspective with day to day life. One young woman wrote the following:

> When I first started experiencing memories of ritual abuse, I was overwhelmed; the images I saw terrified me. Somehow, though, they excited me. I believe I began willing myself to have more and more memories because, as frightening as they were, there was an enormous charge in the suffering. In fact, the more terrifying the memory, the more I could indulge in self-pity, and since self-pity is extremely gratifying, I became obsessed with remembering. It became like an addiction, and eventually the abuse was all I thought about. Soon, the addiction took the place of contact.

The investigation of past memories can become indulgent, and the person does not mature until this indulgence is overcome. The same young woman wrote:

> I would often come to dinner, buried in my pain, and arrogantly expected everyone else to jump right in with me. "If they really loved me," I told myself, "they would hurt because I'm in pain." What I didn't see, however, was that they loved me enough to show me how self-indulgent and selfish I was being by holding on to my pain. They showed me it's important to experience the memories, and to have your feelings about them, but it's equally important to let them go and to get on with your life. I had been defining myself as a victim, and they helped me to realize I could choose not to be. It's that choice that's made all the difference, and has allowed me the freedom to establish relationships, go back to school – to live my life.

In the kind of indulgence this woman described, a person directs more and more attention towards the addiction, and correspondingly less energy towards genuine dialogue with self, others and the world. In self-investigation, one can derive bodily sensations and pleasures and pains from the reliving (or re-creation, or creation) of memories. This can become indulgent and addictive. Probably a biochemical loop is established, (likely involving endorphins, serotonin, dopamine,and other related chemicals) that serves to facilitate the fixation. Such obsessive investigation is akin to becoming lost in a maze. There is often a sickly sweet driven quality to the pursuit, that even can have elements of pleasure. This is much like reading a Stephen King horror novel – you feel kind of ill, but you can't put the book down.

When therapists and counsellors become involved in the revisiting of such memories (or, indeed, sometimes participate in helping to create them), they also may derive an erotic experience from witnessing the horror and wonder of the remembered experience. The investigation can become very indulgent, with the therapists experiencing pleasures and pains in association with their clients. Carl Whitaker used to refer to one-on-one psychotherapy as "emotional incest."[1] Perhaps he recognized the self-stimulating and voyeuristic behaviours that can occur in self-investigation. Therapists can sometimes live their lives through their clients, rather than having the courage to have lives of their own. In crude terms, counsellors are in danger of "getting off" on their clients, rather than being in genuine dialogue with them.

The Uncertainty of Memory

Often, people obtain a good deal of valuable perspective by reconsidering and reliving their life memories. Having done so, they can often put history into order, close past chapters, forgive and move on. But, keep in mind – these are just memories. And the process of memory is a very flawed activity at best. One cannot be certain from one moment to the next what actually occurred. People can only know that they remember this or that. No one can say for sure that it actually happened.

In the professional literature, and in the media, questions have been raised about the validity of repressed memories. Seasoned investigators caution against the tendency to believe all memories to be true, thus abandoning discriminating intelligence. This is nothing new: Freud himself was acutely aware of the problem.[2] On the other hand, now that "false memory syndrome" has been named, there is danger of a backlash, where no one's memory is to be believed. There is a fine line here. Surely there is a middle road that allows for the importance of the memories without becoming fixated upon them.

Memories Induced by Therapists

Next, there is the consideration of therapist-induced memories. The problem is not just that one cannot be certain that what a client remembers is based in fact or not. It is also possible to induce remembrances or attitudes that are not grounded in fact at all. Decades ago, Dr. Herbert Spiegel, a hypnotherapist from Columbia University in New York City, conducted experiments into the implanting of memories. To a client under hypnosis, he spoke a simple sentence, saying that members of the media were involved in communist activities. When the client came out of the hypnotic state, he became distressed, and increasingly agitated, and revealed that he felt a pressure to alert authorities that there was a widespread plot in the media to spread communism. And then he began to name names. Although the original suggestion did not involve names, this person was filling in and embroidering the original statement, with increasingly elaborate detail; he even reported fictitious names as part of his account. It was evident that the person was unconsciously fabricating the story, and was believing it to be true.[5]

How often does this occur in people's day to day life? It seems that individuals can easily pick up on some suggestion, and then embellish or alter it, without conscious awareness. Elizabeth Loftus, an experimental psychologist at the University of Washington, is recognized as an authority on memory.[4] In her extensive experimentation, she noted that the very act of asking a question such as "Was there a barn in the scene that you remember?" would, in time, result in the remembering of a barn in the scene at a later recollection, even though the barn was not remembered until the question had been put. These memories induced by interviewer input have been dubbed "Trojan horses."

> *Through hundreds of experiments performed on some 20,000 subjects, Loftus found that memories could change simply through the questions asked about them. She found that through the fallibility of retrospection she could turn stop signs into yield signs, or make barns appear in a landscape, merely by slipping them into the subjects' consciousness disguised as questions. Unannounced as Trojan horses, these suggestions subtly transformed the memory.*[5]

Even without any intention to manipulate, communication is rife with interpretation. Many counsellors think they know what actually happened in a client's past, and even more frequently they think they know what the client means when he or she is reporting. And yet, the interpretation of what clients remember or report is subject to the errors of the counsellors' own filters, which are coloured by their own experience and attitudes. Most people have had the experience of hearing someone say a word, and then attaching their own significance to the word, and going off on a whole train of ideas related to that word, without checking the person's intended meaning. If someone were to ask whether they knew what the other person meant, they would say with assurance that they did. It is common for people to be sure they know what another person means, without checking. They associate to their own meanings and predetermined interpretations, and then think that their interpretations are fact. When people come from different cultures, there are different meanings attached to even the simplest elements. For example, white often represents purity in North American culture, and thus is suitable for a bride's dress; in Asia, white is frequently associated with death, and traditionally would be most unfitting at a wedding. For clear communication, people must continually check with one another what is meant, in order to achieve optimal (but not perfect) understanding.

We are disturbed by the tendency on the part of professionals to affirm that "If you think you were abused, you were." Therapists are ready to assign child abuse as the cause and problem in many current life situations, and to relentlessly press their clients until they will acknowledge the "truth" of what the counsellor is saying. In Jim Fadiman's words, it becomes "difficult to separate the denied reality from the socially approved of and endlessly reinforced fantasy."[6] In short, some therapists claim to "know" what is true, and then set out to convince their clients. This can become a form of indoctrination; and this process itself is abusive

Avoiding the Witch Hunt
Each culture decrees what is "real." And having established what is real, society determines what realities are "good" and what are "bad." Once that is done, measures can be taken to punish wrongdoers and protect their victims. Frequently counsellors and their clients approach instances and reports of abuse from within this framework, with their focus on determining precisely what happened and then apportioning blame. Commonly, therapists go on a crusade to punish alleged wrongdoers, believing that this somehow helps a person who is not coping in present life. Jim Fadiman writes:

> It is disturbing that psychotherapy seems to be accepting that a deliberate attack on the fantasied attacker will lead to a cure. Have we learned so little from the each-one-murder-one situation in the tattered scraps of Yugoslavia that we need to incorporate tactics of revenge into the process of psychotherapy?[7]

In most cases, when working with clients who report abuse or historical sufferings, we recommend that counsellors not devote so much attention to how much truth there is to the memory nor to the morality of what happened. Certainly, counsellors have a legal obligation to report to the appropriate authorities when there is current danger to a child. But in many cases, the memories pertain to events from many years ago. The important point is this: whatever their clients remember, they can work with the feelings that arise from having such a memory, without having to determine whether or not the memory is real or accurate.

Counsellors can accept their clients' experiences as just that – these are their experiences, and they have feelings and thoughts associated with them that can be honoured. It does not matter so much whether the experiences are factual, or "real." Furthermore, helpers should avoid the diversion of determining what is good or bad (the moralizing overlay on experience). Hence, caregivers should steer clear of the politics of trying to punish wrongs, or tell people what should be so. Counsellors, teachers, and other helping professionals can be fair witnesses to people's experiences, without judging the reality, or the morality of them. In counselling, people are involved in a process of confession and self-revelation. Professionals can be present with their clients, to live through their experiences, in dialogue with them. And they can assist them in becoming free of past experiences and memories. When people become involved in moralizing, or invested solely in political (rather than personal) activity, they may lose an opportunity for freedom, and severely limit their experiences. When professionals do this, then their clients become lost with them. When caregivers perpetuate a limited, fixed viewpoint, the open sky of possibilities will disappear. The task for counsellors is to remain as a fair witness, with feelings and compassion, without judging what is real, or moral, or politically correct. And if helpers find their clients heading down these roads (of morality, political correctness or righteousness), they can call them back to a more nutritive ground, where they can fully experience themselves, and their own feelings and thoughts. If people go down the route of moralizing and political correctness, they are in peril of losing their sense of themselves and others as individuals who have unique experiences and feelings.

When Memories Differ in Families

Some years ago, we reported the case of a young woman who remembers violent and extreme traumas that involve satanism and ritualistic abuse.[8] We also know her sister, who grew up in the same family, and does not remember any such activity. We ourselves don't say that either sister is wrong. We only can say that one sister has these memories, and the other sister does not. What actually occurred, we can never know. The sisters are becoming closer, as they realize that they do not need to have the same memories in order to care about each other. The sister who remembers the abuse wrote the following:

Because my story involves an incredible amount of violence in my childhood, it had only seemed possible to believe that my sister would either present some of the same story, show obvious signs of repression or I would be lying about my version of the story. This had been my belief and my experience prior to being in this environment over time. But I have learned that there is another possibility... that we do each have our own experience. And although there are few if any similarities, we can each be here and learn and grow and heal. I experience such freedom – because it means that I can do whatever I need to do to transform and heal without having to be concerned that the cost would be pain, punishment or vengeance towards others who may or may not be involved in the violence as I have remembered it.

The woman with the memories went through a period of trying to convince others that her family was "bad" and that her memories were "true." She now is moving away from the perspective of blame and weakened victimhood into a stance of responsibility, and is discovering some acceptance for her family. She wrote to us:

I have thought that I wanted people to hate my parents like I did – but in actual fact that would be very difficult. Because I am now seeing that at times I have cut myself off from remembering anything but the pain, and in the pain I wanted revenge. But now over time I have come to open to much more and the hate is not primary. So revenge is no longer the issue. I am very thankful now that you never wanted that either. And that you were always able to encourage me to see the person behind the object. That has been of tremendous value to me. And one of the primary beliefs that I want to bring into my own counselling setting.

She continues,

I find great comfort in knowing that even if I never find peace with my family there is a place or process in which each of our experiences would be accepted. And in that knowing... I too am beginning to accept us all.

Advice to Counsellors from Previous Clients

A young woman who reported memories of severe childhood sexual and ritualistic abuse has now become a therapist herself. She describes her current stance:

I want to respect and have empathy for myself as a person who has memories of incredible violence and a great deal of anger about the events that occurred in my life, but I don't want to move into a position that supports and creates "victims." I have found that this is at times challenging.

She goes on to write the following advice:

I believe that what would be of value to others training and working with people who are viewed as "victims," or in a helpless position, is the value of maintaining the ability to accept and not become judgmental of the people that are involved in the violence or abuse. For myself I hope that I have learned this. Not that I will not judge or become angry – but that I will have the ability to work through these feelings in such a way that allows me to come into the relationship with my client, open not only to their experience but to the experience of the other. Thus I will not make them a victim, but will remain clear about my empathy and support of their own experience within our relationship, but open to the possibility of other experiences. And that if that were not the case I would have the courage to reveal that I may no longer be helpful to the healing process of my client. Because when I begin to believe only their experience we both become limited and closed. It is difficult enough to live with my own sense of guilt about the things I have said my parents did. But if I not only have to accept and move inside my heart, but also then must try to open the heart of someone who my story may have impacted – then the work becomes a great deal harder.

A Balanced Perspective

There is a possibility of erring on either side of this controversial issue. Counsellors can dismiss all memories as not being based in fact, and thus disallow the individual's experience. Or they can go on a righteous rampage to punish perpetrators of remembered past traumas. Let us not make either error. Caregivers can live along with their clients and friends who remember the most hideous things, empathize and work with them, without having to get caught up in whether or not the memories are true, or with apportioning blame.

21 **"Truths" (Not) To Live By**

Self-help and popular psychology and spirituality appear everywhere today, on television, in books, and on the internet. Whether expressed as quick-fixes on TV, in the byte-sized chunks of inspirational and motivational quotes, or in the offices of counselling professionals, these ideas are all around us. Often there is little real discussion or questioning of them, with sometimes serious consequences for people who try to live by them. The following is a sampling of notions we think are in danger of being reified into "truths." Our comments on them are intended to stimulate discussion and investigation, rather than themselves becoming more "truths" to live by without question.

Change Is Possible

This assumption, if held unthinkingly, can lead to all sorts of problems. Common sense and experience show that people are limited by their basic nature and biological assets or handicaps. When people work against their basic structures or try to discard or fix what they see as undesirable parts of themselves, they frequently cause themselves much misery. For us, the important issue is not change, but rather people's relationship to situations. Becoming aware of this provides individuals with an opportunity to transform the expression of their natures, to take more responsibility for themselves and to make freer choices for their future, more realistically based upon the circumstances of the present. We discuss this important distinction between change and transformation in Chapter 17.

Childhood Trauma Will Produce Adult Emotional Problems

This is a widely held notion, especially in the area of childhood abuse. Although many practitioners staunchly believe this — to the point of explaining most, if not all, problems as the result of early childhood trauma — there is little peer-reviewed scientific data to substantiate such claims. However, because of the widespread publicity given to such beliefs, many current emotional problems are being blamed on such experiences. Little investigation has been done into the possibly greater number of people who have used experiences of abuse in childhood to effect positive life choices in adulthood. It would be interesting to discover how and why such people have been able to do so. From our own work we have arrived at the conclusion that the past can inform the present, but should not be used to excuse it. When people adopt this attitude, they can take more responsibility in their lives, and diminish their inclination towards blame and revenge, which tend to arrest personal development. This view does not forgive unconscionable, brutish past violations; instead, it offers an opportunity for the person who experienced such situations to become free of them by avoiding automatic victim roles and behaviours. Indeed, we recommend such an attitude of responsibility in the present to anyone, whether they have suffered abuse or not. Considering oneself a victim of one's past, whatever its nature, severely limits growth in the present.

We Are "Responsible" for Our Illnesses

As we explain in Chapter 12, we believe that each person participates and makes life choices in the process of developing an illness. However, many in the field of holistic health have taken this to mean that people are to blame for their own illnesses; both practitioners and their clients have assumed a moral position around illness. As a consequence, as if they did not already have enough problems, many ill people have in addition had to wrestle with a guilt and self-blame that is not helpful to them in responding to their situation.

You Are What You Eat

Some people find this dictum so compelling that they become obsessive about everything that they ingest. They appear to lose sight of the human body's amazing ability to sort, choose, absorb and store in accordance with what a person needs (psychologically as well as physically). Rather than spending so much energy investigating every calorie, mineral and molecule that passes their lips, perhaps more could be gained by considering why the body would choose to select the elements it does. Perhaps it chooses to store fat in order to defend the self from intimacy; if so, would it not be more worthwhile for that person to work on relationship issues than on the discovery of ever-new diets? And wouldn't it be interesting to decide on what you eat without a morality of right or wrong? Possibly, it is the moral component of your diet that is most destructive to your health, whether you are vegetarian or carnivorous. Taking the "you are what you eat" argument to absurdity, vegetarians must slowly be changing into plants!

Compromise Is Necessary for a Successful Relationship

Many counsellors believe that in order for a couple to adjust to one another, each partner must give up something in order to reach a compromise. To many this seems like common sense; we think however that what is being advocated is the reduction of each person to the lowest common denominator. Thus, the cost of having a relationship would be for both people to become less of themselves, diminishing the potential of what each person could be. In our experience, many couples that stay together through compromise become increasingly resentful or sink into despair and apathy. Often, they eventually separate with negativism and vengeance.

When partners are responsible for themselves, there is no need for compromise. Instead, they can become curious about differences, and share their varied points of view. Ultimately, they can arrive, not at compromises, but agreements about what course to take, without either partner having to relinquish values or opinions. This is a major theme of our book *Joining: The Relationship Garden*.

Peace Is Possible

Throughout history, it has become apparent that world peace is beyond our grasp. As with most interpersonal relationships, one negotiated compromise after another is temporarily achieved, and then is lost. The only variable is the amount of time between broken agreements and renewed negotiations. During the periods of respite that seem calm on the surface, submerged and repressed resentments breed and grow, ultimately bursting forth in renewed hostilities.

Instead of investing so much time and energy in negotiating new terms for peace, we would do well to focus also on learning to appreciate diversity rather than viewing differences with hostility and suspicion. To do so would require a general acceptance of the principles of self-responsibility and inclusion, both on individual and collective levels. This would make room for more appreciation (as opposed to tolerance) of one another. The past would then be useful to inform the present rather than justify or control it. Instead of repeating old patterns of behaviour, the focus would be on transforming them to create a new sense of harmony with one another.

Rebellion Is Necessary for Independence

Rebellion and independence often seem to go hand in hand; but is this always necessary or desirable? In growing from a state of dependence, rebellion ties the individual to the very tenets that are being negated. Adolescents who rebel against the rule to come home early, for example, are shaping their lives in reaction to authority, hence remaining negatively dependent upon that same authority. In rebellion, the important factors governing behaviour remain located outside of the self.

People can, however, become involved in achieving autonomy rather than independence. An autonomous person's centre remains within the self. Decisions are made on a realistic basis rather than in reaction to somebody else. As Ben has often quipped, "You're mature when you wear your galoshes in the rain, even though your mother told you to do so!" Ironically, many people fighting for their independence really would prefer autonomy, and are disappointed when they achieve an independent state.

People Need Empowering

Empowerment is frequently espoused as an antidote to past grievances and oppression. Unfortunately, the attitude represented by this term often perpetuates a system of victimhood and blame. Society acts to punish transgressors and reward victims, who can then feel powerful in their revenge. In the end, we wonder what actually has been gained. What are the rewards of revenge?

In Chapters 2 and 3, we distinguished between power (having control over external events and others) and strength (which involves confidently accepting and expressing oneself); the former is other-related while the latter is self-referred. To our way of thinking, then, to have power and dominance over others is actually a position of weakness because of the dependence on the submission of others. On the other hand, when people have an internal sense of strength, they are more full and authentic. Power diminishes the self; strength stimulates growth.

High Self-Esteem Is Important for Personal Success

As we explained in Chapter 4, we think the achievement of high self-esteem is overrated, and its pursuit potentially dangerous.

We recommend instead that people learn more self-acceptance and self-compassion – to be more ready to acknowledge and love themselves in their struggles to survive and belong. To have the initiative to try, to accept themselves if they fail, and to rely upon themselves as the judges of what is deemed success – these are the hallmarks of individuating people. We discussed this process in detail in Chapter 1. We know many people with rather low self-esteem who are creating happy lives for themselves, because they have learned the secret of self-acceptance!

Shame Causes Unhappiness

There is much confusion regarding shame and guilt, which are frequently interchanged in usage and dictionary definition. To us, it is guilt, not shame, that underlies many of the problems people have in life. We make a particular distinction between guilt and shame, which is different from that of most other commentators. We discuss this in some detail in Chapter 3.

When people are in guilt, they are punishing themselves for a breach of conduct that violates a law or a moral tenet (either real or imagined); they are less of themselves in the objectification and self-hate that accompany guilt. Guilt is associated with the problems of striving for perfection which we outline in Chapter 3. In guilt, people are cold, tight, distant, objectified and objectifying; they thus are not standing forth in their authentic nature. Guilt involves a closure of the self; hence, the myriad problems that come with withdrawal can ensue.

On the other hand, in our terms, shame is an experience of warmth that involves self-recognition; it is a personal response to being revealed, where the reference is to the self. In shame, people are undefended and vulnerable, and hence capable of intimacy and growth; with the revelation that accompanies shame, people can be more aware of themselves. So, indeed, shame involves a sense of fullness about the self, and can accompany a deep happiness.

Bad Things Only Happen to Bad People (and Good Things to Good People)

This statement is a symptom of a limited viewpoint that is rooted in morality rather than awareness. Underlying this notion is the propensity for people to ascribe guilt before wrongdoing is actually proven. Related to this is the frequently misinterpreted karmic idea that each person is atoning for wrongs committed in the past. The simplistic moral corollary is that doing good ensures a good life. Would that it could be so simple!

As we suggested above, the concept of personal responsibility is often misused to mean that each person is to blame for all action and results (hence "bad" occurrences are the punishment for bad people). This moralistic twist is often misapplied to illness conditions. That you are responsible for your illness or accident (i.e., you have participated in the lifestyle that contributes to everything in your life) does not mean that you are to blame for the illness. So, people cannot be assessed as "bad" based upon what has occurred with them.

You Can Attract What You Will

Variations on this idea have a long history, but it has most recently come to popularity through the 2006 film *The Secret* and the subsequent book of the same name. *The Secret* has received a very positive response from many people, some of whom apparently see it as a tool for acquiring wealth and personal advancement. The basic notion is that what you place your attention upon will manifest in reality. An oversimplification is that we create and manifest our own reality; wealth and power are within the grasp of anyone who learns and applies the secret.

But even without such self-serving and materialistic attitudes, the "law of attraction" on which *The Secret* is based seems to have some worrying implications. One is that if you have an accident or disease, it's your fault. Similarly, if a community is devastated by a flood, or a country by famine, did those people bring it on themselves?

To us, the law of attraction is a perversion of a notion that we find more sage and comprehensive (and which we wrote about at length in *The Illuminated Heart*). This is the Confucian concept of the Will of Heaven. In this view, there are forces and influences that one can learn to resonate with, thus entering more of the flow of the universe. This is also a fundamental notion of the *Yi Jing* or *Book of Changes*. When one understands the changing dynamic patterns of events and how they are made manifest, one can conduct oneself in ways that enhance life and vitality.

A simple example of this is that when you understand that living things require water to survive, and learn to resonate with the way water and plants behave, you will be more in harmony with the nature of the universe. Knowing this, you will naturally water your house plants when they are dry, and they will thrive; so too will you thrive in the healthy environment in which you are an active participant. On a larger scale, through understanding and learning to resonate with one's environment and the people in it, one can contribute through one's actions to the creation of a healthier life for all.

This is very different from *The Secret*, which would seem to imply that you simply set your mind to a healthy house plant, and the universe will do the rest. The law of attraction suggests that you can do this just by placing your attention on the desired outcome and believing it will happen. The same goes for having wealth, abundance, and power. In the short run, you often can get what you want through personal will and effort; but if you don't participate in a responsive way with the whole system, and with others, the gains are limited by being self-serving and are often not enduring.

People Are Essentially Good (or Essentially Bad)

People have debated the question of our essential or basic nature for millennia and have tended to come down on one side or the other, asserting either that we are basically good or basically bad.

However, it seems that either way we choose, once human behaviour is divided into "good" and "bad" through moral beliefs, social convention attempts to eliminate the bad. The "bad," the dark, and the negative forces within are generally repressed and denied; then people see no need to address them. Instead, society holds up an unrealistic "ideal" type of person whom all citizens are expected to use as a model for their own behaviour. Usually people adopt this denial, refusing to address themselves to the inherent "evil" capabilities that lie within them; this leads to the expression of the repressed energy in indirect (and frequently socially acceptable) ways – such as wars, petty crimes, ruthless interpersonal relationships, dirty politics, and exploitative kinds of businesses that ignore personal and ecological considerations.

We ourselves take more of an existential than essentialist view of this question. People are not basically good or bad. Rather they are capable of the whole spectrum of moral behaviour. It is important for people to know and acknowledge this, so that they can choose how they wish to exist in the world.

Get Out of Your Head; Trust Only Your Body!

This was the rallying cry of many who lived in the rebellious era of the 1960s and 1970s. It made thinking politically incorrect, and remnants of it persist to this day. The mind was held suspect while the body, its functions, meanings, and feelings were held in high regard. Responsibility and cause-effect considerations were devalued, as adherents to such a philosophy wanted to live "in the moment," impulsively catering to emerging desires. Information, history, theory, books, philosophy, and literature (all products of the mind) were relegated to the dustbin, thus fostering an epidemic of anti-intellectualism, anti-planning and anti-commitment. This situation prepared the way for the next, more profound denial, "You are not your body, or your mind."

You Are Not Your Body Or Your Mind!

This is the maxim of the spiritually ambitious who wish to grow beyond themselves through transpersonal methods, such as those proposed by gurus of Eastern religions and philosophies, and in a Western version amongst fundamentalist religious ideologies. All the uses of the will are seen to contribute towards illusion and earthly desire (sin and worldliness in a more Western frame), preventing the person from experiencing the "oneness" of universal consciousness or the purity of salvation. Adherents to such transcendental ideas frequently find living and supporting themselves in regular society to be distasteful or difficult; hence they may gather in "spiritual" and "intentional" communities that support their spiritual quest. In their rejection of society's traditional standards, their search for "oneness" results in a degree of social isolation.

People (Especially Children) Need to Be Loved

This belief is likely impossible to dispel. It is based on the assumption that "love" is a commodity – that people are born deficient, needing to be filled with love, first from parents and then from other people. We think that children need to be stimulated – but they do not need to be loved! Most people live as though they will only be happy when they obtain a dependable source of love; most carry with them a sense of being entitled to love, and resent parents and partners who do not provide what they expect. Yet, they are actually only going to feel fulfilled when they discover their own ability to love, realizing that there is no such thing as "love"; there is only the activity of "loving," a feeling that is only growth-inducing when it emanates from them, not when it comes to them. Depending on love from without seems to provide security; but this attitude results in issues of control, and does not foster the development of autonomy. We have much more to say about this in *Joining: The Relationship Garden*.

Other People Can Hurt Our Feelings

Although much of people's behaviour is governed by this belief – fearing that what is said may hurt another's feelings, or believing that what others do or say will hurt their feelings – actually, the mechanism for creating emotional pain exists solely within the individual. Whatever is said or done by anyone else, it is the individual's own interpretation of the deed or word that stimulates the brain to initiate whether to laugh or to hurt. The trigger exists primarily within the recipient's brain centres. So, more accurately, people hurt their own feelings over what others say or do – it is impossible for it to be otherwise! We discuss this view further in Chapter 10 on the communication model, where we also explore some of its practical implications for relationship.

Let Your Feelings Be Your Guide/Trust Your Intuition

Feelings enhance the texture and quality of experience and can provide a person with useful information. However, since they are directly dependent upon our perceptions and interpretations (as we outline in Chapter 10), feelings by themselves are an insufficient source upon which to base decisions. People would be better served by developing more accurate perceptions and checking out the accuracy of their judgments. Since feelings are generated on the basis of perceptions and interpretations and are so context-based, they are readily affected by prejudice and past events, experienced when individuals may have arrived at conclusions that might not be helpful in the present. Thus, making decisions in the present based solely upon feelings is generally unwise. Some people interpret this admonition as meaning "trust your intuition," using what is sometimes called the "sixth sense." In some rare people, this sense is highly developed, so that it is perhaps worthy of some trust; but, for most people, this is not the case.

If You Really Understood, You'd Agree

This is a very common belief in interpersonal relationships. It is based upon an arrogant concept that one's own perceptions and judgments are so "true" that if other people really understood your perspective, there is absolutely no chance that they could arrive at another (especially an opposing) opinion. Frequently, one can fully understand another person's point of view and still not agree with it. At those times, even though the person who understands makes no claims to being "right," the other person will argue, apparently believing that if others understood, they could not do other than to agree. In our experience, it is possible to understand, to disagree, and to still remain close to another person.

People often say, "I just need to be heard." Frequently, we suspect that what they actually mean is more like, "If you really hear me, you will agree with me." We think there is great value in being present for a person, listening carefully, and attempting to understand things from their point of view; however, it is not necessary to agree with them or see things the same way. Empathy and caring do not require agreement.

Good Communication Ensures a Long-Lasting Relationship

Some research into the current high divorce rate suggests that good communication is not a definite indicator of which couples remain together; what seems more important than their style of communication is the intent to remain together and a basic level of good will.

Often people make "communicating properly" more important than attending to the people in the relationship. This can occur with our own communication model as with any other style of interaction. People may stick to the "letter of the law," but ignore its spirit, most often by overlooking the principles of vulnerability and curiosity. In this way, they may use the model more as a tool for control and aggression than a path towards intimacy.

Clear communication cannot guarantee that people will stay together. Indeed, as people become clearer with one another, they may make well informed decisions not to remain in relationship. Having said all this, for us and for many people who want to form intimate and enduring relationships with one another, the communication model we have developed has been a vital support.

Jealousy Will Destroy a Relationship

Jealousy is a feeling related to anxiety about the possible loss of a valued person to someone or something else. It is often an expression of unresolved insecurities from past childhood experiences. When jealousy arises in intimate relationships, it can be seen in a positive light:

- It is an expression of how important and meaningful the other has become to the jealous person.

- It reveals areas of fixation and immaturity within the jealous person; often these have previously been hidden or denied.

- It can signal a readiness for the jealous person to share with the partner those areas of vulnerability.

- When these feelings are shared without the element of control, intimacy can grow stronger and both partners have the opportunity to grow, individually and together.

Jealousy becomes destructive when people blame their insecurity and pain upon another, and when they use their hurt to control others. An example of a basic blame message is, "I am hurting because you are showing attention to her." The usual controlling option would be, "My pain is being caused by you – so stop seeing her and pay more attention to me!"

The sharing pain option is different: "I want you to know about my pain without your having to change anything about yourself. I am exploring my sense of insecurity, and want to share with you what I discover. In the meantime, I want to hear about your attraction and desire for her. Also, I want to check your intentions."

By choosing the latter option, both partners are capable of becoming more responsible, with a golden opportunity for personal growth. Using jealousy for control will invite hostility and distance between them.

Intimacy Equals Sexual Excitement

People are capable of experiencing a great variety of sexual feelings. What is usually called "sexual excitement" is related to an objectifying symbolic system that carries an underlying story of pursuit and capture. A commonly held assumption is that, as intimacy develops, the sexual excitement will grow. In practice, this is most often not the case. Certainly, at the beginning of a romance, when people are relatively unknown to one another, there is often a high level of sexual excitement. However, over the years, as these lovers learn more about one another (familiarity), or have really come to know one another (intimacy), their sexual excitement usually wanes.

That sexual excitement tends to decrease with time and familiarity or intimacy (as we define it) can be the source of much anxiety, disappointment and frustration for many couples. Often, they interpret the diminishing sexual appetite as a sign of some problem in their relationship. It may in fact indicate a high level of shared intimacy. It may mean that because they know one another so well, they are having difficulty in objectifying one another. This is a common problem. It signals a need for partners to be creative and curious about one another, to deepen intimacy while rekindling sexual excitement as they choose. We have much more to say about this in *Joining: The Relationship Garden*.

Parents Should Stay Together for the Sake of the Kids

Children probably flourish best in a loving environment (whatever that may be). Frequently people judge that to be a particular family configuration (usually a two parent family, with a mother and a father). Nowadays in North America, however, more than half of the children are either raised in a single parent family, or with one parent who is not blood related. Does this spell trouble for our future generations?

We think not. In our experience, couples that stay together "for the sake of the kids" can create an unstable, unloving family environment. Even though the basic needs for accommodation and food may be met, the general atmosphere can be confusing. Although the children might never say, they can experience the lack of caring between the parents, the possibility of hostility and conflict (both open and covert), the differences over how the children are to be handled (or not handled, as in many instances), and the lack of real communication between all members of the family. Furthermore, children have a tendency to blame themselves for their parents' differences.

When parents stay together under these circumstances, children have a daily opportunity to feel bad about themselves.

We generally encourage couples to work through difficulties together and in the process create more healthy and loving environments for themselves and their children. However, sometimes separation may be the best option. When parents separate with consideration and respect for one another, the transition can be made easier. Parents who are separated or divorced can both creatively provide their own consistent presence to the children, in their own fashion.

22 Spirituality, Religion and Meaning

Most people will wrestle with issues of spirituality and meaning, regardless of their particular problems and their motive for embarking on a voyage of self-discovery, personal growth, or self-healing. The fields of education, religion, psychology, sociology, and politics also must ultimately address the issue of spirituality. From a holistic or structural point of view such as we outline in Chapter 17, the spiritual dimension reflects the state of being of the other levels of each person's existence; when there are fixations at any level, these will be manifested spiritually too. Although a person's awareness and focus may be on one of these levels, any movement or change will find expression on all of the levels. Thus, shifts in body, emotions, or mental attitudes will have spiritual implications; and conversely, alterations on the spiritual plane will be manifest mentally, physically and emotionally.

For us the term "spirituality" refers to the aspect of being that addresses the issues of meaning. Frequently, spirituality is confused with religion, which we take to be a codification of spirituality. Religion is a sort of map of meaning that is used by institutions and governing authorities to provide a group of people with a morality – rules of behaviour and thought aimed at a common goal. As such, religion has a tendency, in Alfred North Whitehead's phrase, "to degenerate into a decent formula wherewith to embellish a comfortable life."[1] We ourselves are not religious; however, we have studied many religions to find the nuggets of spirituality upon which they are based, and to understand the social conventions that people adopt to embrace deeper meanings in their lives. We agree with Coleman Barks, who writes:

> I am not opposed to churches. There is a deep human value in the rituals they provide. I love to enter the sacred space of a church, and also that of a mosque, a synagogue, a Hindu temple, the space described by standing stones, and the high mountain retreats of Bhutan. The singing and the friendships found in these communities can be very beautiful. It is just that the turf-squabbling of the organized religions has become hazardous to the health of a wider community and maybe to that of the planet itself.[2]

Our own perspective is humanistic, and we find our richest meaning in human interactions and relationships. We are reluctant to invoke notions of God to explain important phenomena; yet, we acknowledge that for many people, language that involves a deity is a meaningful way to speak of significant things. We have worked with religious people of many persuasions, and find theology a worthy field of study.

We encourage people to discover their own personal sense of meaning, whether it comes in religion, or in the arts, or science, or in nature, or in human relationships. To us, the grandeur of a sunrise evokes similar feelings to the lofty sensations we feel in a grand cathedral or temple; we also find similar feelings in the majesty of a fine symphony or the breathtaking wonder of a trained dancer. For us, however, meaning is most deeply discovered in an intimate relationship of the kind we have described in this book and elsewhere. In our own relationship we have discovered strength and meaning and a sense of connection with what we have called universal energy and others might identify as spirit, or God. As the line from *Les Misérables* has it:

To love another person is to see the face of God.[3]

The distinction between religion and spirituality is crucial to such a perspective. In the West, many people suffered from unhappy church experiences in childhood, and so they resist any exploration in the direction of spirituality; we think they confuse religiosity with spirituality. Their resistance is often based in their belief that spirituality will be accompanied with morality, control, limitation of their behaviour, guilt, recrimination, self-denial, and ultimately self-denigration. Often, such a belief is based on experiences arising out of the teachings of what has been called redemption-based spirituality. In this view, meaning is found in the belief that humans are imperfect in sin, and need to be redeemed through the intercession of an external agent.

This view assumes a higher power (God) existing outside the self. Hence power, control, and morality are issues to be discovered beyond oneself, dictated by a wiser, stronger, and invulnerable being. The authority for correct behaviour exists with that being ("God") or the agents of that being ("church"). Redemption-centred spirituality offers redemption or enlightenment through renunciation, atonement, self-denial, or disengagement from the material, physical world; salvation offers relief from guilt, pain, and suffering. Spiritual practices in redemption-centred spirituality are often transcendental in nature, through self-denial, self-punishment, or disengagement from oneself. The goal is to get beyond the reality as it is. In terms of the power-strength continuum we described in Chapters 2 and 3, this is fundamentally a power-based approach to spirituality. Most people, in their struggle toward autonomy and personal growth, must reclaim the strength and personal integrity that they lost in their upbringing and social training. The authorities that they have most often rejected include parents, education, and religion. When people reject religion, their resistance is commonly centred on questions of authority and right and wrong. However, in their rejection of religion, people frequently become locked in a power struggle themselves, which tends to obstruct their growth, rather than aid it.

There is another possible view of spirituality, in which the authority remains within the individual. This has been named by some as creation-centred spirituality, in which each person is seen as a part of, and reflective of, the totality of existence ("God").[4] This view is closer to our own perspective, and seems to us more conducive to the development of strength (as opposed to power). In this view, each person is already whole, although the wholeness is usually not clearly expressed. There is nothing to be rid of, or added to, or punished for; there is only more self-awareness and self-responsibility to be experienced. There is no need to struggle toward perfection; each person is already whole. Instead of striving, people can devote themselves to know and to accept themselves in the process of self-compassion. In this way, they can be more revealed to themselves and to others, manifesting what already exists within. This is a practice of revelation and unfolding wholeness, rather than a striving toward a perfection dictated by greater authorities. People then can be involved in creating the expression of themselves, and are released from the obligations to become what others want them to be.

These issues related to external authority have had a significant impact on the lives of most people, whether they had direct early experiences with a religion or only grew up in a society dominated by religious ideas. As we have seen, denying religions or reacting against them is not much help; such actions tend rather to fixate a person's energy all the more, creating more walls and resistances that produce more blocks. Often when people drop out of formal religions, they seek some other expression of their spirituality. In North America, people are sometimes drawn toward Eastern religions, which offer the promise of liberation. Ironically, too often the very people who are attempting to escape from the tyranny of authoritarian rule will submit to the authority of a guru or another form of religion (perhaps the teachings of a New Age leader) in the hope of finding enlightenment or absolute truths.

However, as we have seen, a spirituality is possible where the authority for meaning remains centred in each individual. Alternative meanings or even opposing points of view can be considered, sorted, and digested; no one position need be swallowed whole or taken on as "the truth." The universe is a whole, expressed uniquely in each being. If this wholeness is considered to be God, then, each individual being is a distinct expression of God. Consequently, each person may be considered as whole, capable of discovering personal meaning or individual truth from within. Our task is not to become God, or to fashion ourselves to please God, but rather to *discover* God (the elements of meaning of the self) within. As an expression of a structuralist philosophy, such a spirituality would have us discover the patterns of existence (or God) in any of our levels of being – in our bodies, our feelings, our minds, and our relationships.

To us, it is not necessary to invoke "God" in such a system, though many do – rather, we take the central theme to be the discovery of meaning. In this, Buddhist psychology and existential philosophers might agree.

Sin, Separation and Connection

Redemption-centred spirituality assumes that we are born imperfect or incomplete (in sin) and that we need to make reparations and submit to a higher power to become perfect; this is the moral interpretation of sin (we are "imperfect" or "bad"). In so-called creation-centred spirituality each person is believed to be whole, connected to all others and the universe, as part of a total energy flow; however, because of a limited state of consciousness, the experience of being connected is lost; sin (meaning "separation") is the state of being unaware of that connection. In redemption-based spirituality, human life is rooted in "original sin"; in creation-centred spirituality, human existence emanates from "original blessing."

The goal of creation-centred spirituality is therefore to rediscover that connection, reaffirming the wholeness of existence through self-awareness; the authority remains within the person, not in others or in outside structures or institutions. Creation-centred spirituality is thus self-centred (as we define the term in Chapter 2) but is not selfish, self-indulgent, or self-promoting. God (or meaning) can be found in all of life's experiences, including those that appear to be negative, dark, and frightening. Relationships with others are prime contexts for rediscovering connection and thus transforming separation or "sin."

Spirituality in this sense emphasizes living more fully in the present, acknowledging all aspects (both dark and light) of the person, becoming more self-aware, with a higher level of consciousness. The goal is to embrace reality as it is, rather than transcend or deny it as tends to be the case in redemption-based approaches. In this context, learning through relating is a *transformational* approach; discovering creative expression of all aspects of the person is one of the goals. Spirituality can be experienced at all levels of being, at all times. God can be expressed by each man and woman being fully alive, as free of fixations as possible, willing to allow the energy flow into all niches of experience, without bias or prejudice. Spirituality of this sort acknowledges a oneness, with responsibility but not license. This is the "every-minute Zen" notion of being fully present and fully aware, rather than striving toward perfection.

We encourage people to pay attention to all aspects of their being, including the spiritual. We ourselves have discovered our own spirituality in the daily work and pleasure of our relationship together and in fellowship with others.

Epilogue

We agree with the Eastern philosophers and some existentialists who posit that the human being is suspended somewhere between the earth and heaven, facing the need to survive while yearning for a felt sense of meaning, some reason to survive. Since survival needs seem to be best served through belonging to groups and organizations, each individual frequently finds the demands of the self at odds with the demands of society and culture. Individual development reflects that dynamic tension. Most often, the self is sacrificed for conformity and security; however, the inner yearning for fuller expression of that self cannot be completely extinguished.

Throughout history, many different kinds of political systems have encountered that irrepressible desire for freedom of expression of the self. When the self cannot be fully expressed, the cost is enormous, although often subtle and disguised. These disguises may take on a wide range of symptom formations at all levels of being – emotional, spiritual, mental, physical and environmental. At root is a common thread of isolation and anxiety resulting from a separation not only from others, but also from ourselves! It is our contention that much of human endeavour is aimed towards healing those separations; it is also our experience that most people lack many of the basic tools to effect such a healing. Instead of exercising personal responsibility, many people tend to ascribe power and authority to others, thus limiting their own development. We believe that the project of establishing a meaningful dialogue in a relationship of intimacy can be a most fruitful way to overcome isolation and rediscover our connection with ourselves, with each other, and with the cosmos.

We are tiny beings in a vast universe, challenged to find meaning in our lives. We believe that people's significance is to be found with each other, in connection and communion. We subscribe to the notion that we are alone and have the job to individuate; at the same time, relationships are vitally important to find our place in the whole. This dichotomy is the human condition. In one way, we are separate and alone, seeking contact, while in another way, we are a part of everything, and only need to let go and accept our participation and belonging.

This paradox can be resolved through relationship and dialogue. Thus, the programs we developed that are taught at The Haven focus on relationships as the core issue for individual development. Although our singular lives can seem so small, the possibilities in relationship with others are vast.

We hope that this book has provided you with some of the understanding and tools for you to use to heal your own personal rifts, and has contributed to the development of some faith in yourself. You are not alone! We ourselves derive comfort in the notion that we are participants in something far greater than our solitary lives. In this vein, we end with one of our favourite poems:

Oceans

I have a feeling that my boat
has struck, down there in the depths, against a great thing.
And nothing happens!
Nothing ... Silence ... Waves ...

Nothing happens?
Or has everything happened,
and are we standing now, quietly, in the new life?

— Juan Ramón Jiménez[1]

Notes

Part I: The Discovery of Strength

1   Morris West, *Shoes of the Fisherman* (London: William Heinemann, 1963), p. 204.

1 THE FAILURE OF SUCCESS

1   K. Horney, *Neurosis and Human Growth: The Struggle Toward Self-Realization* (New York: W.W. Norton and Co., 1950) and T. Rubin, *Compassion and Self-Hate* (New York: David McKay Co., 1975).

2   Horney, *Neurosis and Human Growth*, Chapter 3, "The Tyranny of the Should."

2 THE POWER-STRENGTH CONTINUUM

1   Paul Tillich, *The Courage to Be* (New Haven: Yale University Press, 1976.

2   G. Bateson, *Steps to an Ecology of Mind* (New York: Ballantine Books, 1972) pp. 271–78.

3   Søren Kierkegaard, *The Sickness Unto Death*, Walter Lowrie, trans. (Princeton, NJ: Princeton University Press, 1941), pp. 43–44.

3 MORE DISTINCTION ON THE POWER-STRENGTH CONTINUUM

1   Rollo May, *Love and Will* (New York: W.W. Norton, 1969), p. 100.

2   Joseph Fletcher, *Situation Ethics: The New Morality* (Philadelphia: The Westminster Press, 1966).

3   D.B. Rinsley, "The Developmental Etiology of Borderline and Narcissistic Disorders," in *Bulletin of the Menninger Clinic:* 44(2), 1980, p. 127–134.

4   John Bradshaw, *Homecoming: Reclaiming and Championing Your Inner Child* (New York: Bantam Books, 1990), p. 47.

5   For example, TED talk "Listening to Shame," March 2012. www.ted.com

6   Lama Anagarika Govinda, *The Psychological Attitude of Early Buddhist Philosophy* (New York: Samuel Weiser, Inc., 1974), p. 121, and Jock McKeen and Bennet Wong, *The Illuminated Heart: Perspectives on East-West Psychology and Thought* (Gabriola Island: The Haven Institute Press, 2012), p. 233–4.

7   C. Ricks in C.D. Schneider, *Shame, Exposure, and Privacy* (Boston: Beacon Press, 1977), p. 109

8   D.H. Lawrence, *Aaron's Rod* (Harmondsworth: Penguin Books, 1950), p. 200.

9   Oscar Wilde, in Edgar A. Levenson, *The Ambiguity of Change* (New York: Basic Books, 1983), p. 33.

10   M. Buber, *Hasidism and Modern Man*, edited and translated by Maurice Friedman (New York: Harper Torchbooks, 1966), p. 180.

5 ENTITLEMENT

1   Alfred Adler, quoted in Ira Progoff, *The Death and Rebirth of Psychology* (New York: McGraw-Hill, 1956), p. 81.

2   M.S. Mahler et al., *The Psychological Birth of the Human Infant: Symbiosis and Individuation* (New York: Brunner/Mazel, 1976).

3   Jock McKeen and Bennet Wong, *The Illuminated Heart: Perspectives on East-West Psychology and Thought* (Gabriola Island: The Haven Institute Press, 2012), Chapter II.3.

4   S. Cashdan, *Object Relations Therapy* (New York: W.W. Norton and Co., 1988), p. 44.

Part II: In the Face of Anxiety

1   André Malraux, quoted by Maurice Friedman in *To Deny Our Nothingness* (New York: Dell Publishing Co., 1967), p. 17.

6 EXISTENTIAL ANXIETY

1   José Ortega y Gasset, *The Revolt of the Masses* (New York: Norton, 1957), pp. 156–157.

2   P. Tillich, *The Courage to Be* (New Haven: Yale University Press, 1976), p. 41.

3   R. May, E. Angel and H. Ellenberger, eds., *Existence: A New Dimension in Psychiatry and Psychology* (New York: Basic Books, 1958), p. 62.

4   R. May, *The Meaning of Anxiety* (New York: W.W. Norton and Co., 1977), p. 208.

5   P. Shaffer, *Equus* (Harmondsworth: Penguin, 1977), p. 107.

6   H. Gardner, *Frames of Mind: The Theory of Multiple Intelligences* (New York: Basic Books, 1983).

7   Georges Bernanos, *Diary of a Country Priest*, translated by Pamela Morris (New York: The Macmillan Co., 1937), p. 108f.

8   Patrick Overton, *The Faith Poem*. www.patrickoverton.com.

8 FROM OBJECTIFICATION TO INCLUSION

1   D. Rinsley, "The Developmental Etiology of Borderline and Narcissistic Disorders," Bulletin of the Menninger Clinic, 44(2), 1980, p. 129.

2   E. Becker, *Denial of Death* (New York: The Free Press, 1973), p. 146.

3   M. Buber, *I and Thou* (New York: Charles Scribner's Sons, 1970).

4   S. Freud, *Civilization and its Discontents* (New York: W.W. Norton and Co., 1961).

5   Thomas Szasz, *The Meaning of Mind* (Westport, Connecticut: Praeger Publishers, 1996).

6   W.G. Heard, *The Healing Between: A Clinical Guide to Dialogical Psychotherapy* (San Francisco: Jossey-Bass, 1993), p. 78.

7   M. Buber, *The Knowledge of Man: Selected Essays*, M.S. Friedman and R.G. Smith, trans. (Atlantic Highlands, N.J.: Humanities Press, 1988), p. 71.

8   C.G. Jung, *The Collected Works of C.G. Jung*, translated by R.F.C. Hull (Princeton, NJ: Bollingen Foundation and Princeton University Press, 1966), vol. XVI, par. 454.

Part III: Relationships

1   Rainer Maria Rilke, quoted in John Welwood, *Journey of the Heart* (New York: Harper Collins, 1990), p. xiii.

9 INTIMACY

1   Based on Rilke, *Letters to a Young Poet*, #7: "Love... consists in this: that two solitudes protect and border and greet each other."

11 ANGER: AN EXAMPLE OF SHARING FEELINGS RESPONSIBLY

1   Joann S. Peterson, *A Book about Anger, Boundaries and Safety*, Haven Institute Press, 2006. See also G. Bach and P. Wyden, *The Intimate Enemy* (New York: William Morrow and Company, 1969).

2   These assumptions also underlie our Dynamic Empathy Model and the gestalt cycle, both of which we describe in *The Illuminated Heart: Perspectives on East-West Psychology and Thought* (Gabriola Island: The Haven Institute Press, 2012).

Part IV: Health and Healing

1   D.H. Lawrence, *The Complete Poems of D.H. Lawrence*, edited by V. de Sola Pinto and W. Roberts (New York: The Viking Press, 1971), p. 620.

12 LEARNING IN ILLNESS AND HEALTH

1   Rudolf Virchow quoted in K. Menninger, M. Mayman and P. Pruyser, *The Vital Balance* (New York: Viking Press, 1963), p. 41.

2   D. Connelly, *Traditional Acupuncture: The Law of the Five Elements* (Columbia, MD: Center for Traditional Acupuncture, 1979) and our own *The Illuminated Heart: Perspectives on East-West Psychology and Thought* (Gabriola Island: The Haven Institute Press, 2012), Part IV.

3   V.E. Frankl, *Man's Search For Meaning* (New York: Simon and Schuster, 1962), p. 97.

4   Ibid, p. 76.

5   An example from our own experience is "Yogic Bliss" in Bennet Wong and Jock McKeen, *In and Out of Our Own Way*, (Gabriola Island, B.C.: PD Publishing, 1995), pp. 34–35.

6   Robert Duncan, in *The New American Poetry* edited by D.M. Allen (New York: Grove Press, 1960), p. 403.

7   Ernie McNally, personal correspondence.

15 DISENGAGING DEPRESSION

1   J. Mitchell, *The Selected Melanie Klein* (Harmondsworth: Penguin Books Ltd., 1986), pp. 150–151.

2   Judith Viorst, *Necessary Losses* (New York: Simon and Schuster, 1986).

3   Linda Nicholls now offers an extremely useful program at The Haven called Depression: Conscious Alternatives.

16 ENERGY CONCEPTS

1   W. Reich, *Selected Writings* (New York: Farrar, Straus and Giroux, 1973), p. 53 and our *The Illuminated Heart: Perspectives on East-West Psychology and Thought* (Gabriola Island: The Haven Institute Press, 2012), Chapter II.6.

2   R. Wilhelm and C.F. Baynes, *The I Ching, or Book of Changes* (Princeton: Princeton University Press, 1967), p. 235.

3   R. Feitis, ed., *Ida Rolf Talks About Rolfing and Physical Reality* (New York: Harper and Row, 1978).

4   Wilhelm and Baynes, *The I Ching, or Book of Changes*, pp. 280–81.

5   L. Von Bertalanffy, *General Systems Theory* (New York: Macmillan, 1984), p. 45.

6   Bennet Wong and Jock McKeen, *A Proposal for a Dialogical Understanding of Acupuncture Therapy*, presented at the 6th International Congress of Chinese Medicine, San Francisco, April 28, 1997.

Part V: Issues and Opportunities

1   James Bugental, *The Search or Existential Identity* (San Francisco: Jossey-Bass, 1976), p. 1.

17 CHANGE AND TRANSFORMATION

1   R.L. Stevenson, *Familiar Studies of Men and Books* (1882).

2   Jock McKeen and Bennet Wong, *The Illuminated Heart: Perspectives on East-West Psychology and Thought* (Gabriola Island: The Haven Institute Press, 2012), Chapter V.3.

3   Ken Wilber, *A Brief History of Everything* (Boston: Shambhala, 1996), p. 30.

18 BEYOND THERAPY

1   Edgar Levenson, *The Fallacy of Understanding: An Inquiry into the Changing Structure of Psychoanalysis* (New York: Basic Books, 1972).

2   Ibid, p. 70.

3   Ibid, p. 174.

4   R. Hycner and L. Jacobs, *The Healing Relationship in Gestalt Therapy* (Highland, NY: Gestalt Journal Press, 1995), p. 65. See also Jock McKeen and Bennet Wong, *The Illuminated Heart: Perspectives on East-West Psychology and Thought* (Gabriola Island: The Haven Institute Press, 2012), Chapter II.16.

5   Edgar Levenson, *The Ambiguity of Change* (New York: Basic Books, 1983), p. 164.

6   Ibid, p. 106.

7   *The Fallacy of Understanding*, p. 67.

8   In particular Denise Goldbeck has led her hugely successful program Kids in the Spotlight (originally Dance and Games for Kids) at The Haven for more than 25 years, and David Raithby and Linda Nicholls offer the extremely popular Teens Alive programs.

9   *The Fallacy of Understanding*, p. 223.

19 FROM SURVIVAL TO DISCOVERY

1   Bennet Wong and Jock McKeen, "A Case of Multiple Life Threatening Illnesses Related to Early Ritual Abuse," Journal of Child and Youth Care, Special Issue, 1990, pp. 1–26.

2   James Hillman, *Suicide and the Soul* (Dallas: Spring Publications, 1976), p. 23.

20 MEMORIES OF ABUSE

1   Carl Whitaker (1912–1995) was a psychiatrist and pioneering family therapist who taught at The Haven in the 1980s. His approach was iconoclastic, and he sometimes shocked participants with unexpected statements that frequently cut through to the heart of the matter.

2   Jock McKeen and Bennet Wong, "Memories of Abuse: A Call For A Balanced Perspective," Journal of Child and Youth Care, vol 10, no. 3, 1995, pp 67–81 and *The Illuminated Heart: Perspectives on East-West Psychology and Thought* (Gabriola Island: The Haven Institute Press, 2012), Chapter II.1.

3   M. Métivier and S. Kleinfeld, producers. "Mistaken Identities," shown on The Fifth Estate, CBC Television, Autumn, 1993.

4   Elizabeth F. Loftus, "Creating False Memories," *Scientific American*, September 1997, pp. 71–75.

5   Kathryn Robinson, "Memories of Abuse," *Seattle Weekly*, August 11, 1993, p. 22.

6   Jim Fadiman, "Overcoming Abuse," *Perspective*, July/August 1993.

7   Ibid.

8   Bennet Wong and Jock McKeen, "A Case of Multiple Life Threatening Illnesses Related to Early Ritual Abuse," *Journal of Child and Youth Care*, Special Issue, 1990, pp. 1–26.

22 SPIRITUALITY, RELIGION AND MEANING

1   Alfred North Whitehead, quoted in M. Fox, *Original Blessing* (Santa Fe: Bear and Company, 1983), p. 10.

2   C. Barks, *A Year With Rumi*. New York, NY: HarperOne, 2006, p. 10.

3   From the musical *Les Misérables*, by Alain Boublil and Claude-Michel Shönberg, lyrics by Herbert Kretzmer (Original Broadway Cast Recording, Geffen Records, 1986).

4   M. Fox, *Original Blessing* (Santa Fe, NM: Bear & Co., 1983).

EPILOGUE

1   Juan Ramón Jiménez, in Robert Bly trans., *News of the Universe* (San Francisco: Sierra Club Books, 1980), p. 105.

Index

Items followed by [P] or [S] refer to definitions of terms used on the power-strength continuum described in Chapters 2 and 3.

Absence [P] 49
Abuse, sexual or physical
    and adult emotional problems 203–204
    and dislocation in time 77, 78–79
    memories of 195–202
    options in the wake of 183–194
Acceptance. *See* Five A's, the
Acceptance [S] 48
Achievement [P] 39
Acknowledgment. *See* Five A's, the
Action. *See also* Five A's, the
    difficulty taking, in MS 135, 139–140, 145, 147
    in the Communication Model 110–111
Actual Self 21–31
Acupuncture 145–146, 161–164
    The Needles Are Not the Point 164–166
Admiration [P] 53
Allergies 27, 64, 80, 127–133, 156, 171
Aloneness [S] 50–51
Anaclitic depression 153–155
Anger
    and depression 152–153
    different from violence 112
    pursuit of, in abuse therapy 189–190
    responsible expression of 112–116, 141, 148, 185–186
Anxiety
    and allergies and phobias 129–130, 132
    and anger 113
    and enemy-making 88–89
    and intimacy 95–96
    and location in space 79–81
    and location in time 77–79
    and medication 81–82, 127

and MS 139, 142
and objectification 85–86
dealing with: the power-strength continuum 32–33, 37, 39–40, 42, 45
existential, neurotic, and psychotic 69–74, 153, 173, 195
Appreciation. *See* Five A's, the
Arrogance 211
Assertion 115
Attention [P] 39
Authenticity [S] 49
Authentic Self 21–31
Autonomy [S] 40–41, 41
Awareness. *See* Five A's, the

BAAAAA. *See* Five A's, the
Barks, Coleman 215
Becker, Ernest 86
Being and non-being
    33, 38, 50, 54, 69, 70–71, 73, 87, 170
Being [S] 38
Black/White Thinking [P] 46
Blame. *See also* Self-hate, Anger
    and entitlement 63
    and jealousy 212
    and MS 136–137
    apportioning, in cases of abuse 199–202, 203–204
    different from responsibility 48–49, 179, 204, 207
    expression of 98, 101, 114–115, 185–186
    in power-strength distinctions 42, 48–49, 53, 151, 159, 206
    the path of, in self-hate cycle 26
Blame, Being to [P] 48–49
Blame [P] 42, 48
Blocks. *See* Fixation
Boredom 149, 156

Boundaries. *See also* Boundary illnesses
  and anger 112, 114
  with children 62
Boundaries [S] 49
Boundary illnesses 27, 64, 80, 128–130
Bradshaw, John, and toxic shame 46
Brown, Brené, views on shame and vulnerability 46–47
Buber, Martin 54, 87, 90–91
Bugental, James 167

Cancer 126, 134, 148, 156
Caretaking [P] 42, 143
Caring [S] 42
Change. *See* Transformation, and change
Charge [P] 52. *See also* Sexuality, objectification and charge
Child within 184–185
Chinese medicine
  allergies and phobias 129
  and depression 149–150
  and energy 121–122, 162, 163, 164
  and MS 141
Clarke, Susan 103
Clearing 99, 155
Come Alive 9, 164
Communication
  and depression 154, 155–156
  and healing 125–126, 148, 154, 165–166
  the Communication Model 91, 104–111, 211–212
Communications Paradigm (Levenson) 176–178
Confucius 47, 208
Context
  in the Communication Model 104–106
  primary contextual location 76
Control [P] 37–38
Curiosity 101, 104, 107
Cynicism [P] 53

Dance and Games for Kids. *See* Kids in the Spotlight
Death 17, 50, 69, 73–74. *See also* Grief and loss
Depression 149–158
  anaclitic 153–154
  and anger 115–116
  and change and transformation 169, 171–172
  and self-hate 26, 152–153
  cyclical/bipolar 156–157
  medication for 157–158
Desires/Choice [S] 47
Divorce 155–156, 213–214
Docks (fixation in time) 77–78
Dodge, Wayne 25
"Dumping" (different from clearing) 99

Educational
  approach to helping relationships 181–182
  perspective on depression 151
Emotion
  and sentimentalism 52
  emotional fixation 122
Empathy 63, 101, 155, 159, 179, 186, 211
  different from sympathy 36, 42
  Dynamic Empathy Model 225
Empathy [S] 42
Energy concepts 159–166. *See also* Qi
Enlightenment 19
Entitlement 61–65, 216–217
Ethics, Personal or Situation [S] 45
Eureka 181
Excellence [S] 54
Existentialism 32–33, 38, 69–70, 220
Expectations 22–24, 99–100, 113–114

Failure
  and self-hate 24, 30, 57
  of success, the 21–31
Failure to thrive 153–154
Faith [S] 50

Feeling, Genuine [S] 52
Feelings, in the Communication
     Model 108–109
Fewster, Gerry 11
Field Awareness [S] 41
Field dependency 24, 35, 36–37
  and autonomy 40
  and energy concepts 159–160
  and entitlement 63–64
  and field awareness 41
  and location 79
Field Dependency [P] 40–41, 41
Five A's, the 28–29, 60, 73, 91, 153
Fixation 83–84, 121–124, 160–161,
     165–166
  and spirituality 215
  and the five A's 28
  in time (docks) 77–78
  on memories 78, 195–197
Flashbacks. *See* Docks
Forgiveness 197, 204
Frankl, Victor 123
Freud, Sigmund 88, 175, 197
Fulfilment [S] 52

Gestalts, incomplete 152–153, 155–156
Gestalt therapy 177
Ghosting (projection) 99
Glory, the path of, in self-hate cycle 26
Goldbeck, Denise 227
Gossip 115
Grey, Shades of [S] 46
Grief and loss 44, 152–153, 155–156
Guilt 42, 81, 100
  guilt feelings around abuse 193
Guilt [P] 46–47, 206–207

Harmony 208
  and peace 205
Helplessness, the path of, in self-hate
     cycle 26
Heuristic education 181
Holy [S] 53
Hope [P] 50

Horney, Karen 21, 23
Humility [S] 53
Humour [S] 39
Hurt feelings 47, 96, 109, 210

Ideal Self 21–31
Inclusion 64–65, 90–91, 179–180
Independence [P] 41
Individualize [P] 41
Individuate [S] 41
Indulgence 52, 62–63, 195–197
Insecurity [S] 39–40
Inspiration [S] 53
Intention
  in the Communication Model 110
Intimacy 95–103
  and sexuality 95
  creating and maintaining 97–101
  different from familiarity 101
  related to power-strength
     continuum 95–96
Intimacy [S] 38
Irony [S] 53
Isolation [P] 38
I-You/I-It relationships (Buber) 87,
     90–92, 96, 97

Jealousy 98, 212
Jung, Carl 88, 92

Kids in the Spotlight 227
Kierkegaard, Søren 37
Klein, Melanie 150

Lawrence, D.H. 52, 117
Lemon, Judy 154
Levenson, Edgar 175–182
Location 72, 75–84
  in space 79–81
  in time 76–79
  primary contextual 76
  using symptoms for 120
Loneliness/Isolation [P] 50–51
Love, and loving 44, 92, 93, 103, 210

Mastery 30–31, 39, 41, 54, 58
Mastery [S] 39
May, Rollo 44, 69
McNally, Ernie and Cathy 126
Meaning
  and depression 149–151
  and meaninglessness 69–70, 72,
     220–221
  and spirituality 123, 215–219
  in the Communication Model
     (interpretation) 106–108
  meanings of disease 120–121, 144,
     146–147
Meditation 123, 177
Memories
  of abuse 183, 184–185, 186–187, 188,
     191–192, 195–202
  without fixation 82
Mirroring 57, 58–60, 181
Misérables, Les 216
Monologue, autologue, and
     dialogue 90–91
  From monologue to dialogue in the
     Communication Model 104,
     107
Morality. See also Right and wrong
  and abuse 190–191, 199–200
  and change 169–170
  and guilt 46
  and religion 215
  and the sacred 53
Morality [P] 45

Narcissism
  and entitlement 61–62
  culture of 176
  primary 86
Needles are Not the Point, The 164–
     166
Nicholls, Linda 49, 154, 226, 227
Nietzsche, Friedrich 123
Non-being [P] 38

Objectification
  and abuse 183
  and sexual charge 100, 213

from, to inclusion 85–89
Objectification [P] 38, 99
Object relations 86, 128–129
Obligations [P] 48
Obsessing 70, 72–73, 204
Ontic/ontological anxiety. See Anxiety,
     existential, neurotic, and
     psychotic

Pain, Accept Pleasure and [S] 44
Pain, Minimize [P] 44
Peace 205
Perception in the Communication
     Model 106, 109, 210–211
Perfection [P] 54
Personal, Being [S] 38–39
Personal [S] 44–45
Peterson, Joann 112, 154
Phobias 64, 80, 127–133, 156
Pity [P] 42, 184, 194
Pleasure, Maximize [P] 44
Political [P] 44–45
Power-Strength Continuum
  Absence <--> Presence 49
  Achievement <--> Mastery 39
  Admiration <--> Inspiration 53
  Attention <--> Recognition 39
  Being to Blame <--> Being
     Responsible 48–49
  Black/White Thinking <--> Shades of
     Grey 46
  Blame <--> Acceptance 48
  Charge <--> Fulfilment 52
  Control <--> Vulnerability 37–38
  Cynicism <--> Irony 53
  Field Dependency <--> Autonomy 40
  Field Dependency <--> Field
     Awareness 41
  Guilt <--> Shame 46–47
  Hope <--> Faith 50
  Isolation <--> Intimacy 38
  Loneliness/Isolation <-->
     Aloneness 50–51
  Minimize Pain, Maximize Pleasure
     <--> Accept Pleasure and
     Pain 44

Morality <--> Personal or Situation
    Ethics 45
Non-being <--> Being 38
Objectification <--> Being
    Personal 38–39
Obligations <--> Responsibility 48
Perfection <--> Excellence 54
Political <--> Personal 44–45
Pride <--> Humility 53
Rebellion <--> Standing Forth 51
Role <--> Authenticity 49
Sacred <--> Holy 53–54
Security <--> Insecurity 39–40
Self-Hatred <--> Self-Compassion 43
Selfish <--> Self-Centred 42–43
Sensitivity to Being Hurt <-->
    Sensitivity to Others 47
Sentimentalism <--> Genuine
    Feeling 52
Seriousness <--> Humour 39
Shoulds/Injunctions <--> Desires/
    Choice 47
Standing out<---> Standing forth 34–
    36
Submission <--> Surrender 51–52
Sympathy/Pity <--> Empathy 42
Taking Care of Others <--> Caring
    about Others 42
Trust Others <--> Trust Self 53
Victimhood and Blame <--> Self-
    Responsibility 42
Walls <--> Boundaries 49
Power-Strength Continuum,
    introduction 32–34
Presence [S] 49
Pride [P] 53
Procrastination 139–140
Projection 88–89, 99
Psychoanalysis 175

Qi (energy) 121–122

RAD 153–154
Raithby, David 227
Reaction [P] 50
Rebellion [P] 51

Recognition [S] 39, 161
    and shame 46
Reich, Wilhelm 161, 165, 177
Religion 215–219
Resonance 160–161
Response [S] 50
Responsibility [S] 48
Responsible, Being [S] 48
Right and wrong
    and climate change 124
    and diet 204
    and enemy making 88–89
    and power-strength 45, 48
    and religion 217
    and the Communication Model 106–
        107
Roles [P] 49
Rubin, Theodore 21

Sacred [P] 53–54
Secret, The (movie and book) 207–208
Security [P] 39–40
Self-Centred [S] 42–43
Self-Compassion 27–31, 43, 101, 206
    and self-esteem 57, 60
Self-Compassion [S] 43
Self-Esteem 57–60, 206
Self-hate 24, 43
    and depression 152–153, 155
    and MS 135, 137, 139
    and self-esteem 60
Self-Hate [P] 43
Selfish [P] 42–43
Self-Responsibility [S] 42
Sensitivity to Being Hurt [P] 47
Sensitivity to Others [S] 47
Sentimentalism [P] 52
Seriousness [P] 39
Sexuality. See also Abuse
    and depression 156
    and MS 140–142, 147
    different from intimacy 95, 100, 213
    objectification and charge 87, 91–92
    submission and surrender 51–52
Shadow (Jungian) 88–89
Shame [S] 46–47, 206–207

Shoulds/Injunctions [P] 47
Should, tyranny of the 23
Sin 216, 218–219
Solitudes, two 73, 95, 102, 104
Standing Forth [S] 34–37, 51
Standing Out [P] 34–37
Station, Waiting at the 17–18
Structuralism 175
   Structuralist education 181–182
   Structuralist Paradigm 178–180
Submission [P] 51–52
Surrender [S] 51–52
Sympathy [P] 42
Szasz, Thomas 90

Teens Alive 227
Tillich, Paul 33, 69–70
Transcend and Include (Wilber) 173
Transcendence 170, 216–217
Transformation, and change 169–174,
      180, 203
Trust Others [P] 53
Trust Self [S] 53

Universal Energy 159–161, 216

Victimhood [P] 42
Violence. *See also* Abuse
   different from anger 112
   no violence in responsible expression
      of anger 114
Viorst, Judith 150–151
Vulnerability
   Brené Brown's discussion of 46–47
Vulnerability [S] 37–38

Waiting at the Station 17–18
Walls [P] 49
Whitehead, Alfred North 215
Wilber, Ken 173
Will and willfulness 137

Yoga 123
Zen 219

Made in the USA
Lexington, KY
27 December 2018